LESLIE COM[...]

Dearest Minnie

A SAILOR'S STORY

Travel with
Teddy Roosevelt's
Great White Fleet
1907-1909
through 200+
full color postcards.

JOHN E SHERIDAN ——08

*To Midge ~
Enjoy this journey ~
Leslie Compton*

Historically accurate, inspired by real-life events

Dearest Minnie, a sailor's story

Travel with Teddy Roosevelt's Great White Fleet
1907-1909 through 200+ full-color postcards

by Leslie Compton

Dearest Minnie, a sailor's story is a fictionalized account based on the experiences of real people, and which is historically accurate as far as what is known about the voyage of the fleet.

ISBN-13: 978-1937333393

ISBN-10: 1937333396

Cover and book design by Suzanne Parrott

Cover image adapted from the Sunday Magazine of the New-York Tribune, *"The Letter Home" by John E. Sheridan, Feb 9, 1908*

Photography (magazine cover, author Leslie Compton) by William G. Compton

Illustrations, postcards and photos used with permission by
The Naval Historical Foundation, Washington, D.C.

and from the private collections of

Les Cowman of Victoria, Australia,
Dr. Steve Levine, DDS, New Jersey, and
Leslie Compton, Oregon.

Library of Congress Control Number: 2017938696

historical fiction; Great White Fleet; U.S. history; postcard collections

FSP
FIRST STEPS
PUBLISHING

First Steps Publishing
PO Box 571 • Gleneden Beach, Oregon 97388-0571
www.FirstStepsPublishing.com

ACKNOWLEDGMENTS

This story is historically correct. I have used Maurice as the narrator, adding my research to the letters written on the backs of post cards sent to Minnie.

After spending six years of research, traveling up and down the east and west coast to learn about a period of history I knew little about; this book has finally come to fruition.

I want to give special thanks to the Rockland-Bergen Postcard Club in New York. Without their encouragement and support I would never have begun this project. Thank you Grady Overstreet for your search through libraries and historical societies in Southern California.

There were many postcards created to celebrate the tour of the Great White Fleet. I have included only a small number. Two very generous people shared their collection of Great White Fleet postcards and have allowed me to include them in this book. Steve Levine of New Jersey invited me, a total stranger, to his home to view his cards. Those I wished to use in this book were copied and sent to me. Many of the Japanese cards belong to Steve. Thank you.

A very special thanks goes to Les Cowman of Victoria, Australia, who after communicating on the Internet was kind enough to put his elaborate collection of White Fleet postcards on a CD, detailing every card—an amazing effort, thanks Les.

Lieutenant Commander, USN, James R. Reckner, (Ret), author of *Teddy Roosevelt's Great White Fleet* graciously took time to read my first draft to correct any historical errors. Thank you for taking time out of your busy schedule.

Thank you Suzanne Parrott of First Steps Publishing, who believed in this book, who believed in me.

And finally a special thanks to my ex-husband for without his support this book would not be in your hands. He never complained as night after night dinner would be late or not at all; laundry not ironed or beds not made. He never left me during times of ranting and raving when the computer would not cooperate or I had misplaced a footnote, forcing me to re-number the whole manuscript. Thank you, Joe.

CONTENTS

ACKNOWLEDGMENTS 3

PROLOGUE 5

COMPOSITION OF
THE GREAT WHITE FLEET 10

ITINERARY OF THE GREAT WHITE FLEET 11

HISTORICAL BACKGROUND
FOR THE GREAT WHITE FLEET 13

HAMPTON ROADS 23

TRINIDAD 31

EN ROUTE TO RIO DE JANEIRO 40

RIO DE JANEIRO 48

PUNTA ARENAS, CHILE (SANDY POINT) 55

CALLAO, PERU, LAND OF THE RISING SUN 60

MAGDALENA BAY 67

SAN DIEGO, CALIFORNIA 72

SAN PEDRO, CALIFORNIA 77

SANTA BARBARA, CALIFORNIA 82

SAN FRANCISCO, CALIFORNIA 88

WASHINGTON 104

HAWAI'I 112

AUCKLAND, NEW ZEALAND 118

SYDNEY, AUSTRALIA 124

MELBOURNE, AUSTRALIA 132

ALBANY, AUSTRALIA 142

MANILA 145

JAPAN 147

CHINA 163

BACK TO MANILA 168

EN ROUTE TO COLOMBO 172

COLOMBO, CEYLON 174

SUEZ 179

GIBRALTAR 185

THE RETURN TO HAMPTON ROADS 191

EPILOGUE 196

STATISTICS 198

ENDNOTES 199

BIBLIOGRAPHY 206

POSTCARD LIST 209

PROLOGUE

"Cousin Min died today," my father announced as he settled at the dinner table one cold February evening in 1952.

"Cousin Min? Was she the old lady we visited last summer in a nursing home on the way to Grandpa's ranch?" I asked as we began passing the meatloaf and vegetables.

"Yes, she's the one," Dad answered.

A picture of Cousin Min immediately flashed through my ten-year-old mind, and I gulped down my milk. I could still see her laid out flat in bed, her face covered with deep wrinkles. Expressionless eyes stared at the ceiling while her mouth formed a perfect permanent letter 'O.' Only the rising and falling of her chest told me she was still alive. A sea of similarly occupied beds surrounded her in a large, oversized room. The short cries and moans emanating from those lifeless creatures echoed throughout the corridor. It had been my first experience in a nursing home, and I wasn't looking forward to any future visits.

"Who was Cousin Min, Dad?" I asked. Dad put down his fork, pushed back his chair and began his discourse on that branch of our family tree.

"Cousin Min was my father's cousin . . ."

Minnie Camp was born in Tompkinsville, Kentucky on April 11, 1870 to Sterling Camp and Ellen Glazebrook. Sterling Camp, was a musician and a stringed instrument maker, while his wife had a talent for music and a college degree. The Glazebrook family was the first to bring musical concerts and theater to the small Kentucky community after the Civil War. Given their parentage, it was only natural that Minnie and her younger brother, Frank, developed a love and talent for music. As young children, Min and Frank learned to play the piano along with the stringed instruments their father crafted, the mandolin, violin, viola and the guitar. Besides his music Frank became fascinated with photography and dreamed of opening his own studio. Minnie was a very intelligent lady, Dad recalled, and was not shy about expressing her opinions. Sitting in the parlor working on needlework samplers with the other society ladies was not Minnie's style. Creating music, taking nature walks, going on adventure trips or nurturing her garden, those were some of Minnie's favorite pastimes.

In November 1887, a general store in Tompkinsville owned by Min's Aunt and Uncle Nelson was robbed and set on fire. The fire quickly spread through the town leaving most of the business section in ashes. The culprits were apprehended, but the Nelsons decided not to rebuild. Instead, they pulled up stakes and headed west to make their fortune in California, settling in Tulare where they opened a furniture store. A few years later, Min's Aunt Emma Glazebrook Gist and husband Frank left Tompkinsville to make a new home in Santa Ana. Then in 1903, my Grandfather, William Compton, and his brother Clarence also migrated from Kentucky to the riches of Southern California, settling in Bakersfield. Seeing that half of the family had relocated to the West Coast, Frank and Min decided to use the inheritance money they had recently received from their Grandfather Glazebrook to pack up and head west. They settled in Kern City, just outside of Bakersfield.

Growing up, my father rarely mentioned Cousin Min before that night in February. I only remember other relatives holding sketchy memories of a bitter old lady with a high-pitched nasal voice. So, the declaration of her death had no real effect on our normal dinner conversation that chilly evening.

A few months after Minnie Camp's death, a series of packages arrived from her estate addressed to me. In one of the boxes was a child's porcelain tea set; the delicate china was painted a hot pink with gold edging on the rims of the cups and saucers. A scene from the early 1800's was painted in the center of each cup. Opening the other cartons, I found three old, elaborately decorated albums full of picture postcards. Paging through the albums, I was intrigued by the old photos of faraway places from around the world. I carefully placed the albums back into their cardboard boxes and stacked them on my closet floor along with the clothes I neglected to put away.

When I left home to create a life of my own as an adult, the boxes of postcards moved with me. Each time I relocated, I would unpack the cartons and re-examine the colored pictures of scenes that had captured my imagination so long ago.

In the early 60's, I decided it was time to dump the postcard albums I had been lugging around. I met a vendor at an antique street fair selling— among other things— postcards. "Aha!" I thought. "I'll sell my cards to him and make lots of money." I invited the gentleman to my apartment to look over my collection and —hopefully — make me a generous offer.

At the prescribed time, the antique dealer arrived at my home. After an hour looking through my collection of postcards he had the audacity to announce the average price per card he was willing to pay was 25 cents. "A few of the cards are worth $2.00 apiece, but others are only worth a nickel. And," he continued, "many are simply worthless." I couldn't believe what I had heard. My thought of making a fortune quickly evaporated. But something else suddenly became clear for me: I realized I could never sell Minnie's postcards, not to him, not to anyone. Cousin Min's life was all wrapped up in those pictures of faraway places. A woman I knew almost nothing about was sitting before me hidden in between the messages and the color photos. I showed the gentleman to the door.

Years went by; marriage, children and job transfers moved me to many different locations. Always the carefully packed boxes of postcards traveled with me.

A few years ago, after settling into our new home in North Carolina, I again unpacked the boxes containing the old postcard albums. The bindings had lost most of their glue. The pages were torn and beginning to disintegrate. I carefully took out the cards, threw away what was left of the albums, and settled down to reread their messages. I found many of the cards had been sent to Minnie from relatives now deceased, but the postcards from foreign countries were all signed with unfamiliar initials. I separated the cards with the unknown signature into chronological order to find they had been written between 1907 and 1910. Many of the later cards had been stamped with a naval postmark, *USS Virginia*.

After weeks of investigation, I discovered most of these cards had been mailed during Teddy Roosevelt's cruise of sixteen battleships around the world, later coined the Great White Fleet. It wasn't long before I became consumed with the research of that event and its relationship to Minnie Camp. To learn more, I subscribed to postcard publications, joined a postcard club and frequented postcard shows within driving distance of my home. Uncovering the mystery of the unknown initials took several years. I located John Maurice Blair as their owner. Through my travels and research, Cousin Min slowly began to emerge as a vibrant, beautiful young woman with a fascinating story to tell.

John Maurice Blair was just the kind of man the Navy was seeking. He was born in Tompkinsville, Kentucky and attended the one room brick schoolhouse with Frank and Minnie Camp. The Blairs were farmers living on a rented piece of land outside of town. He was a shy, quiet young man. Early in his life he developed a love for music, enjoyed the beauty of nature, fishing and swimming. As he became more proficient playing his horn, he joined the Tompkinsville band that gave summer concerts in the park and marched in holiday parades. He was also fond of listening to Minnie play the piano in her parlor, and often Frank and Minnie would ask Maurice to join them in their musical performances.

As a young boy, Maurice took a fancy to Minnie. He enjoyed their long walks from school, sometimes teasing her by pulling her long curls. When they were older, he and Minnie ventured on the worn paths along the Cumberland River. Over the years, Maurice's feelings for Minnie grew from a childhood playmate to feelings of passion and adoration, but those sentiments were never verbalized. Minnie had so many interests in her life that she was unaware of her friend's heartache.

Life in Tompkinsville was quiet and predictable. Maurice was young and restless with a spirit for adventure. But he was resigned to stay in that small Kentucky town after high school because his mother and Minnie were there. He worked in town as a laborer and, when time allowed, helped on his family's farm.

In 1904, everything changed for Maurice. Minnie and Frank packed up their belongings and headed West to join other members of the Glazebrook family in Southern California. Minnie left Tompkinsville with no idea of the feelings Maurice felt for her. He was devastated. Word circulated that the Navy was recruiting in Hopkinsville, only a short train ride away. Their new slogan, "Join the Navy and see the world" began calling him. With his love of the water and adventurous spirit, it made perfect sense for him to join the Navy. This would be his chance for adventure, a chance that he knew he would otherwise not have if he elected to stay in Kentucky.

On March 4, 1904, Maurice and a buddy boarded the train in Tompkinsville, traveled to Hopkinsville, and signed up for a three-year hitch with the Navy. Maurice was told that because of his age and proficiency in music, he could enlist as a musician and earn a bit more money. A musician recruit had to be between the ages of twenty-one to thirty-five years old. (1) Maurice would receive $32.00 a month with twenty cents taken out for Naval Hospitals. Each good-conduct medal, pin or bar would increase his monthly pay by seventy-five cents. This sounded fine to Maurice, after all, a coal passer seamen 3rd class was paid only $22.00 a month.

Maurice spent the next three years on the East Coast performing with the ship's band for naval ceremonies and practicing maneuvers and drills. He was disappointed that his tour of duty was limited to the waters of the Atlantic. When the *USS Virginia* was completed in 1906, Maurice was transferred and remained on that ship for the duration of his naval career.

Occasionally Maurice would send a postcard, or postal as they were called, to Frank or Minnie in Kern City to let them know how he was getting along. According to the only member of the family still alive at the time who knew her, Minnie was not always quick to answer his early cards; she tended to put things off for another day unless it was something to be done in her garden. In fact, some of her relatives felt she was just plain slow!

After his first three years, Maurice grew tired of the Navy's many drills, reviews, and parades. He was also disappointed that he had seen little of the world. In the fall of 1907, he was looking forward to the end of his obligation with the Navy. At this time, rumors about a world cruise began to circulate. This tour sounded like a possible visit to Minnie on the West Coast and a chance to see the far away ports he had hoped to visit when he enlisted. Maurice had no idea of the political ramifications of this cruise, only that it would be the adventure of a lifetime. Maurice again fit the bill for what the Navy wanted. He was quiet, reserved, and intelligent and was a respectable young man with an excellent naval record. He received another incentive to continue in the service with a promotion to musician first class and an increase of $1.36 a month plus the usual $60 for his replacement uniforms. Maurice re-enlisted in March 1907 for another three years.

The Bluejacket's Manual, 1908 states the tour of duty for an enlisted man was four years. However, Maurice signed up for two tours of duty, each for three years.

Minnie began a postcard collection after moving to Kern City. She purchased a leather and abalone-shelled postcard album to place on the center table in her parlor. "It would be wonderful now that you will be traveling around the world," she wrote in one letter, "If you could send me postals of the areas where you visit." This was the opening Maurice had hoped for. After all this time, he had made contact again with his first love. A correspondence soon developed between Minnie, Frank, and Maurice with letters, gifts and postcards.

COMPOSITION OF
THE GREAT WHITE FLEET

December 16, 1907
Rear Admiral Robley D. Evans, Commander

San Francisco, May, 1908
Rear Admiral C. S. Sperry

First Division:

Connecticut - 1907
Kansas-1906
Louisiana-1906
Vermont-1906

First Division:

Connecticut
Kansas
Vermont
Minnesota

Second Division:

Georgia-1906
Virginia-1906
New Jersey-1906
Rhode Island-1906

Second Division:

Georgia
Nebraska
New Jersey
Rhode Island

Third Division:

Minnesota-1906
Ohio-1904
Missouri-1903
Maine-1902

Third Division:

Louisiana
Virginia
Ohio
Missouri

Fourth Division:

Alabama-1900
Illinois-1900
Kentucky-1900
Kearsarge-1900

Fourth Division

Wisconsin
Illinois
Kearsarge
Kentucky

Auxiliaries:

Supply ship: Culgoa
Refrigerator ship: Glacier
Repair ship: Panther
Small yacht: Yankton
Hospital Ship: Relief

Cruisers:

Tennessee
Iowa
Indiana
Texas

ITINERARY OF THE GREAT WHITE FLEET

From Hampton Road, Virginia, to San Francisco, California

Port	Date of Arrival	Date of Departure	Distance to Next Port
Hampton Roads		16 December 1907	1,803
Port of Spain, Trinidad	23 December 1907	29 December 1907	3,399
Rio de Janeiro, Brazil	12 January 1908	21 January 1908	2,374
Punta Arenas, Chile	1 February 1908	7 February 1908	2,838
Callao, Peru	20 February 1908	29 February 1908	3,010
Magdalena Bay, Mexico	12 March 1908	11 April 1908	1,132
San Francisco	6 May 1908		
Total Distance			14,556

Itinerary of the Cruise to the Pacific

From San Francisco to Manila

Port	Date of Arrival	Date of Departure	Distance to Next Port
San Francisco		7 July 1908	2,126
Honolulu, HI	16 July 1908	22 July 1908	3,870
Aukland, New Zealand	9 August 1908	15 August 1908	1,307
Sydney, Australia	20 August 1908	28 August 1908	601
Melbourne, Australia	29 August 1908	5 September 1908	1,368
Albany, Australia	11 September 1908	18 September 1908	3,458
Manila, Philippine Islands	2 October 1908	9 October 1908	1,795
Yokohama, Japan	18 October 1908	25 October 1908	1,811
Amoy, China (Second Squadron)	29 October 1908	5 November 1908	
Manila, Philippine Islands (First Squadron)	31 October 1908		
Manila, Philippine Islands (Second Squadron)	7 November 1908		
Total Distance			16,336

From Manila to Hampton Roads

Port	Date of Arrival	Date of Departure	Distance to Next Port
Manila, Philippine Islands		1 December 1908	2,985
Colombo, Ceylon	13 December 1908	20 December 1908	3,448
Suez, Egypt	3 January 1909	4-6 January 1909	2,443
Gibraltar	31 January- February 1909	6 February 1909	3,579
Hampton Roads	22 February 1909		
Total Distance			12,455

Source: U.S. Navy Department. *Information Relative to the Voyage of the United States Atlantic Fleet Around the World, December 16, 1907 to February 22, 1909.* Washington, D.C.: Government Printing Office, 1910.

(left) Photo #: NH 50477, Lieutenant John E. Lewis, USN, with a mascot Kangaroo on board USS Connecticut (Battleship # 18). The Kangaroo was presented to the ship by the citizens of Sydney, New South Wales, Australia, when the U.S. Atlantic Fleet visited the city in late August 1908.

(below right) Photo #: NH 106193 President Theodore Roosevelt (right) shakes hands with Lieutenant Walter R. Gherardi, Commanding Officer of USS Yankton. Photographed during the President's visit to Yankton on 16 December 1907, as the Atlantic Fleet departed Hampton Roads, Virginia, to begin its cruise around the World. Commander William S. Sims is partially visible at the far right.

(above left) Photo #: NH 106225-KN Neptune certificate of Midshipman Harold M. Bemis, of USS Maine, January 6, 1908.

(right) Photo #: NH 106192 Fine screen halftone reproduction of a photograph showing the Atlantic Fleet flagship, USS Connecticut (Battleship # 18), leading the Great White Fleet's other fifteen battleships out of Hampton Roads, Virginia, at the beginning of the cruise around the World, 16 December 1907.

BATTLESHIP FLEET, LEAVING HAMPTON ROADS, 1907

HISTORICAL BACKGROUND
FOR THE GREAT WHITE FLEET

After the Civil War, America was focused on commerce to rebuild itself. Americans felt confident they were being sheltered from the rest of the world by a small force of cruisers hugging the shores and operating independently of one another.

However, there were a few elected officials who felt as a growing nation America needed better protection from more than just a few naval cruisers to isolate us from the squabbles of world powers. One such man was Theodore Roosevelt. In December 1881, shortly after being elected to the New York Assembly, Teddy Roosevelt summarized his feelings about the Navy in his book debating the War of 1812. ". . . it is folly", he wrote, "for the great English-speaking republic to rely for defense upon a navy composed partly of antiquated hulks and partly of new vessels rather more worthless than old." (2) This belief in a strong navy remained a top priority throughout Roosevelt's political career.

By the end of the 1880's, a basic design for the battleship and the cruiser had emerged using a coal driven steam engine for power. The battleship's design had a central citadel or two, throwing thick black clouds of smoke through several of the tall funnels. Guns of the main battery were mounted in turrets, fore and aft of the central citadel. The steamship's speed and range was limited by the amount of coal it could carry as well as the rate at which the steam engine consumed that coal. (3) Great Britain established its superiority in naval power with Germany and France following close behind.

With the creation of the new steamships arose a need for coaling stations. America, Great Britain, and Germany began to colonize remote locations for their fleets. A disagreement arose between Germany and Great Britain over the Island of Samoa, where America had recently acquired a coaling station. This alerted the United States that they could become involved with European policies even in the Pacific. A growing concern developed for California, fearing she would be exposed to the South American and European navies passing through the proposed canal through the province of Panama (Isthmus Canal.) With the increasing growth of the European navies the protection of being isolated, so long enjoyed by Americans, became inadequate.

Following two failed attempts by the French (1880s) to construct a canal through the province of Panama, the United States commenced building a canal across a 50-mile stretch of the Panama isthmus in 1904.

Meeting this increased need for security was difficult in the 1890's since a backlog of battleships was waiting to be constructed. An American shipyard took two and a half years to install the equipment needed to build one warship. The main obstacle was the production of high-quality steel. The American steel plants were not capable of manufacturing steel armor plates or guns any larger than six inches. To compete with European countries, American battleships had to go abroad to purchase larger guns and armor plate for instillation. For ten years, American manufacturers used eight-inch guns to test European steel trying to locate armor plate that would be superior. Harveyized steel, an alloy of steel and nickel used by the French, passed the required tests and was chosen to become the standard for the American battleships.

These newly created steel ships were dirty and uncomfortable for the sailors. The hot, filthy engine rooms— located below the water line— would sometimes reach temperatures of 150 degrees Fahrenheit. "Every surface was coated with a film of oil mixed with coal dust . . . While the men sloshed around in the water on the floor that cooled the bearings." (4) The third and lowest steam expansion cylinders of the ship's engine were nearly ten feet in diameter and generated 20,000 horsepower which created a constant deafening sound the men had to endure. (5) "The ship design was a fine balance of the competing space and weight demands for fuel, engines, ammunition, and crew accommodations. However, all too often the crew accommodations were short-changed in order to meet other competing demands." (4a) The men were left with only a small space on the gun deck to hang their hammocks each night. Meals were served on bare wooden tables lowered from overhead racks where hammocks had been stored earlier.

The USS Iowa was launched in 1892. Her coal capacity had been increased from earlier battleships. She had a faster cruising speed and carried four twelve-inch guns. Two armored cruisers— the Maine and the Texas— were commissioned in 1895. They were later designated second-class battleships because their main battery turrets were off center putting strain on the hull. That same year, Congress authorized the building of five first-class battleships. These ships had their main battery turrets on centerline to improve the fire arcs as well as the balance of the ship with increased fuel capacity and 12-inch guns. Even with the increased size of their bunkers, (6) these new warships were still restricted to shoreline duty because of their dependency on fuel. The cruisers equipped with fewer guns and using less fuel traveled ahead of the warships and became known as the "eyes of the fleet." (7) The speed of these warships steadily increased as the size of the engines and the battleships increased. But still the American warships were no match for the European navies.

Addressing the Naval War College as Assistant Secretary of the Navy in June 1897, Roosevelt proclaimed the most effective way to achieve peace was to prepare for war, and that meant the expansion of the navy. Many European countries were boasting about their large fleet of warships and laughing at America's cruisers and battleships scattered around the world hugging the shores. Teddy Roosevelt began to formulate his goal of creating a world-class navy by changing tactics from a defensive organization to an offensive one. Congress, with Roosevelt's insistence, went to work and approved the construction of six new armored cruisers and three more first-class battleships, the *Indiana*, the *Oregon* and the *Massachusetts*.

Robley D. Evans was the officer chosen to command the *USS Indiana*. Evans was born in Virginia in 1846. He entered the Naval Academy at the beginning of the Civil War sympathizing with the Union. In 1865, while commanding a company of Marines at Ft. Fisher, South Carolina, a Confederate bullet grazed his chest. A second bullet hit his left leg below the knee, and a third brought him down by smashing his right knee. While on the ground, a fourth took part of a toe. Evans was still able to shoot and kill the sniper responsible for his wounds. Settled in the naval hospital in Norfolk, he heard surgeons talking outside his room about the removal of both of his legs. When an orderly came to see him the next morning, Evans pulled out his revolver, hidden under his pillow, and announced he would shoot the first person who came into his room with surgical instruments. He consequently was left with both legs intact. However, they remained scarred and deformed, causing a limp and excruciating pain for the remainder of his life.

In 1866 Evans regained his commission and, in 1891, was given command of the small gunboat, the *Yorktown*. He received orders to go to Chile where a civil war was raging. Chile was not pleased that the Americans were interfering in their domestic problems. The *Yorktown* arrived to face nine Chilean warships and found Chilean seamen had killed two sailors on shore leave from the *USS Baltimore* and wounded eighteen others with stab wounds. The Chileans made runs at the *Yorktown*, always swerving at the last minute. Evans sent a message: that he had instructed his crew to blow the "boat out of the water and kill every man on her" (8) if one of the Chilean ships even touched the *Yorktown*. The Chilean government issued an apology, and Evans and his crew were able to return home. After this episode, a newspaperman coined Evans with the

4. HABANA.
Maine soon after the wreck. —
El Maine acabado de hundirse.

nickname "Fighting Bob," which stayed with him the rest of his life. Secretly, however, the Navy called Evans "Old Gimpy."

In 1898 support grew in the United States to assist Cuba in an open revolt against Spain. Americans were concerned Spain would remain in Cuba after the proposed Isthmus Canal was built, creating a possible threat. The *USS Maine* was blown apart and sank as she was peacefully anchored in Havana's harbor, killing two hundred sixty officers and men. The United States believed the *USS Maine* had deliberately been destroyed. America declared war against Spain. The slogan, "Remember the *Maine*! To Hell with Spain" was coined and reverberated across the nation. (9) (According to Admiral James Reckner, it is now general agreement that there was a fire in a coal bunker which caused the explosion of ammunition on board the ship.) The war with Spain was the final catalyst that drew America out of its "isolation."

August 12, 1898, the same day the armistice was signed ending the Spanish-American War and releasing control of Cuba, Puerto Rico, the Philippines, and Guam to the United States, America successfully annexed the Hawaiian Islands. In 1899 Samoa and Wake Island were annexed. With the acquisition of these islands, the Navy had to defend them

Teddy Roosevelt was the Assistant Secretary of the Navy during McKinley's administration in 1897-98. In 1899, Roosevelt was elected Governor of New York. McKinley's Vice President died in office, opening the door for Roosevelt to run for Vice President on the Republican ticket with McKinley in 1900. On September 6, 1901, only seven months after taking office for his second term, President McKinley was shot in the stomach while vacationing at the World's Fair. He later died from gangrene developed from the two gunshot wounds. As the new President, Roosevelt was committed to fulfilling his life-long goal of making America a leading sea power with battleships equal to the rest of the world. His plan was to assemble the isolated and scattered ships and have them operate under one command.

Author Robert Hart describes the pride felt by countries with large fleets of battleships: "The battleship, a paradox of power and beauty, demanded attention—the pride and affection of people whose flag it flew and the envy and fear of adversaries. Why hide it in a stockpile? Why not place it on display, as one usually did with costly and beautiful possessions? The meaning of prestige was quite clear to anyone who had watched a parade of battleships." (10)

At the close of the 19th century, the European navies moved from harbor to harbor on a series of cruises. To please the crowds, the ships arrived in formation and steamed into port at high speeds to churn up the water. In unison, they would lower their anchors to the applause of the spectators. The European governments continued to expand these elaborate battle demonstrations to gain public support for their naval expenditures. These visits to neighboring ports were advertised as fleet days with naval reviews and parades. The navies grew larger as each review and parade stretched longer. The American public did not see these fancy reviews from European countries until 1902 when the German Fleet arrived in New York City's harbor displaying her newest battleships.

The European officers soon became restless and upset with the elaborate naval demonstrations for the pleasure of vacationers. New strategies needed to be planned. Several nations debated sending a fleet of ships around the world, (11) but the new battleships were similar to the new automobiles with their troubles and breakdowns. Engineers did not fully understand the workings of the recently installed new devices such as the boiler pressure gauges, cylinders, complex steering levers, the engines for turning turrets, the ammunition hoists, the electrical plants nor the new wireless sets. (10a) With the massive coal consumption (the average of 90 tons of coal every day when traveling at ten knots), and the need for constant repairs, the idea of a cruise around the world was thought to be too risky and was quickly shelved.

In 1906, the *USS Connecticut* and her five sister ships were launched giving America bragging rights with battleships in the Pacific and the Atlantic.

Miniature warships soon found their way into novelty stores around the world. England created a naval war game based on the same strategies as chess using small battleships as pawns. Books were written for adults and children about adventures on the warships and the sinking of other navies. Colorful tins of all sizes and shapes were decorated with paintings of warships. Publishers of postcards saw their opportunity to depict the 'men-o-war' in sets and singles. All nations felt battleships exhibited the best example of

RUSSO-JAPANESE PEACE COMMISSION IN CONFERENCE AT PORTSMOUTH NAVY YARD, U. S. A.
AUGUST, 1905.
The Principals Who Brought to a Close One of the World's Greatest Wars.

power. Magazines and newspapers published rankings of the world's fleets. In Germany, these rankings were printed on decorated charts and sent to all the schools. Not all publications issued the same ratings, but all agreed: Britain dominated the sea with her 45-50 battleships, and France, Germany, and the United States all claimed second place with 20-30 battleships each.

Tensions had been building between Russia and Japan erupting in a war fought in Manchuria and China in 1904. Russia, sensing her defeat, became desperate and sent ten battleships and thirty smaller vessels to Japan to defend her cause. Their speed decreased and the armor belts disappeared when Russia's ships took on sacks of coal and heavily loaded crates of supplies in French Indochina (presently Vietnam). With few ports available for repairs, the engineers had priests pray over "stripped gears and bent rods" to keep the ships afloat. (12) When the Russian ships finally arrived at the war zone, they faced a well-rested Japanese navy and a newly developed explosive mixture called shimose powder. Shimose burned when it exploded, setting even the paint on a steel bulkhead on fire. "Iron ladders were crumpled, guns were literally hurled from their mountings." (13) The Russian ships with their wood decks and paneling lost all but one second class cruiser and two destroyers in less than a day.

Roosevelt organized the peace settlement in Portsmouth between Russia and Japan receiving the Nobel Peace Prize. Japan had lost money and blood during the war and demanded Russia pay for her war debts. America vetoed this request, enraging Japan. This decision provoked the Japanese to become involved in anti-American demonstrations in their country. (14) America's relationship with Japan became strained and unstable.

President Roosevelt was convinced Japan would want to expand into the Pacific after acquiring Korea and Southern Manchuria in the Russian peace settlement. The well-being of America's new possessions, Samoa, Guam, Hawaii and the Philippines became a growing concern. With the near total destruction of the Russian fleet, the massive, fast, big gun battleships became Roosevelt's top priority.

California added fuel to the growing unrest in Japan. Newspapers claimed the high number of Oriental immigrants flocking to San Francisco would soon displace the "White Man." In 1906, San Francisco announced the children of Oriental descent could no longer attend public schools; they would have to attend schools especially set-aside for Mongolians. Rioting erupted against these new constraints in San Francisco as well as Japan. What began as an immigration problem became a war scare.

The war department was informed that Japan had depleted its resources during the war with Russia and wouldn't be able to fight again for another ten years. In light of this information, Roosevelt decided this would be an excellent time for a world cruise. The primary purpose, as stated in Roosevelt's autobiography, was to impress foreign nations and to give Americans confidence in the strength of the U.S. Navy. He felt there was no better way to gain respect from other nations than through a show of force. Roosevelt also believed the Navy needed practice in "navigation, communication, coal consumption, crew stamina, and fleet maneuvering." A cruise would be the best way to perfect those challenges during peacetime so they could be handled during wartime. (15) The naval officers, however, felt the exercises Roosevelt proposed could be accomplished in American waters and saw no reason to push for a world tour.

Congress agreed to a Pacific fleet to maintain the Open Door Policy with China and an Atlantic fleet to protect the East Coast from European factors and from any country that might pose a threat of invasion. Even with reluctance from the officers, Roosevelt ordered the battleships in Europe and South America called home to combine with the North Atlantic Squadron to create a permanent Atlantic Fleet.

After the cruise was announced, rumors began to circulate in the Yellow Press: Japan was ready to take Hawaii and the Philippines. To substantiate his original premise, Roosevelt informed Japan of his peaceful intentions and was told once again Japan was not ready to go to war, but the question remained in the minds of the Americans: if there was a war with Japan, whose side would the powerful British Navy take? The formal alliance between Great Britain and Japan worried Washington. Germany worked to gain American's friendship through gifts and publicity. The Kaiser even offered Germany's battleships for guard duty all along the Atlantic Coast during the cruise, even though he secretly felt the tour would end in disaster.

The Yellow Press (aka Yellow Journalism), is journalism that offers little or no legitimate well-researched news. Instead it relies on eye-catching headlines to sell newspapers.

Problems began mounting against the cruise. The only Navy dry dock facility on the Pacific Coast large enough to accommodate the battleships was in Puget Sound, Washington. America's Pacific territories, Hawai'i and the Philippines, did not have facilities large enough to repair a fleet. Despite these facts, Congress turned down Roosevelt's request to fortify those dry docks.

The warships could not be supplied with coal at sea. With few American colliers, the Navy would have to contract with foreign countries to supply their ships. There had been various requests by the President to fortify coaling stations and eliminate the dependence of foreign colliers. These requests were ignored because many thought during wartime the colliers, having the fuel on float, would be an advantage over coaling stations. This dependence on foreign colliers was a serious gap in the fleet's capabilities. By the end of the cruise, the United States hired one Austro-Hungarian, seven Norwegian and forty-one British colliers to deliver coal to the fleet.

In 1907, America took great pride in their twenty-eight battleships. However, only sixteen of these ships would be capable of steaming on an extended cruise. Of those sixteen ships, six had cracked boiler tubes. The new *Maine* consumed too much coal and was feared to be an embarrassment having to be towed into foreign ports. The *Alabama* had cracks in the piston cylinders, the *Kearsarge* had flammable armor of wood and canvas, and some felt the *Kentucky* wasn't a battleship at all. However, in his Annual Report of 1907, Secretary of Navy, Victor H. Metcalf wrote, "These sixteen ships formed in weight and numbers combined, the most powerful fleet of battle ships under one command in any navy." (16) Four auxiliaries were also chosen to accompany the sixteen battleships on the cruise. Six torpedo boats were assigned to travel a week ahead of the fleet to detect any enemy ambush. These ships were then designated the Atlantic Fleet.

Roosevelt met with representatives of the Joint Board of the Army and the Navy on June 18, 1907, to again discuss the deteriorating relations with Japan. The board felt the Japanese situation did not justify sending the Atlantic Fleet on a Pacific cruise. Roosevelt was also having his problems with Congress; they did not want to appropriate the money. Roosevelt argued he was the Commander-in-Chief and "my decision is absolute in this matter." (17) He told Congress there was plenty of money for the first half of the cruise to San Francisco. If they didn't approve the additional funds, the fleet could just stay in California. He ordered the Navy to be ready to sail by December. Roosevelt wanted the fleet to complete the world cruise before he left office in February 1909.

Rear Admiral Robley Dunglison Evans, a favorite of Roosevelt's, was named the Commander of the Fleet. Evans was still suffering from his Civil War wounds as well as a gouty left foot. Evans' doctor advised against his going on the cruise.

Rear Admiral Charles M. Thomas was selected to be the second in command. He was an overweight man who suffered from heart problems. Thomas had only eight months until he retired from the Navy. His doctors also recommended he not go on the cruise.

Rear Admiral Charles S. Sperry was elected to be third in command. He had recently suffered from an unknown illness that left him very weak. The doctors recommended Sperry stay back until he had fully recovered.

"Fighting Bob," Admiral Robert D. Evans, U. S. Navy.

Rear Admiral William H. Emory was the fourth in command. He had a reputation for entertaining the ladies beyond the call of duty and his retirement was only months away from the date of the cruise. (16a)

These four admirals averaged sixty years of age. The sixteen captains averaged fifty-six years of age. These men were seven to ten years older than foreign officers holding the same rank. While in port during the fourteen months of the world cruise, these officers would have to wear hot, heavily ornamented uniforms in all kinds of weather, make a half dozen speeches a day, eat almost as many meals, and wear a continuous smile. In the evening, they would be required to eat again, drink to numerous toasts and dance with the wives of dignitaries.

Once the ships were in order, and the officers selected, a special campaign was organized to recruit men needed to supply the sixteen ships. The navy's annual desertion rate was nearly twice that of the army. (18) Before this cruise, sailors carried a reputation of being brawlers, alcoholics, and carriers of all kinds of incurable diseases. It was not uncommon to see signs on respectable restaurants and hotels, "Sailors and Dogs not allowed." To give incentives for enlistment, special programs were offered with better pay and recreational activities. The only requirement for an apprentice seaman was to be able to read and write, be of "robust frame, intelligent, perfectly sound and healthy constitution, and free from any physical defects of malformation." (19) The recruiting campaign was centered in the Midwest and the West to attract clean-cut, hard-working, church-going men with rosy cheeks, to impress the foreign countries on the cruise. The Navy was also looking for more intelligent and better educated men than previously recruited. However, nearly three-fourths of all the applicants were ultimately rejected. (18a)

In October 1907, the ships entered naval yards for repairs. Telephone systems and wireless communication devices were installed. The ships were all repainted the customary white, the decks were scrubbed, and the adornments were polished. By November, most of the sixteen battleships were in New York taking on supplies before leaving for Hampton Roads, Virginia. The New Yorkers welcomed the officers and men as though they were already heroes.

Before the fleet sailed, a few eastern newspapers asked for the impeachment of President Roosevelt. These articles said the departing warships would leave the Atlantic coast unprotected, the White House would be burned, and the fleet would be finished off before it reached San Francisco. Roosevelt told the Americans their ports would be protected by the Army's fortifications. The Fleet's purpose was to search out and destroy the enemy on the seas, not to guard the shorelines as they had done in the past. Roosevelt carefully handpicked the newsmen who would travel aboard the ships during the cruise. These reporters were instructed to pass every written word along to pre-appointed officers before submitting any article to their newspapers or magazines back home.

By December 9, 1907, all sixteen battleships headed toward Hampton Roads. Newspapers equated the gathered ships and cruisers in Virginia to a romantic success story. This publicity was another signal to Japan that American was not being aggressive, but was indeed preparing for a good-will tour.

When I began my research for this book eighteen years ago, this was to be the story of the Great White Fleet's Cruise around the world as seen through postcards. After researching Minnie's life and searching for Maurice in my travels around the country, through books, newspapers, postcard shows, postcard clubs, magazines, and the Internet; this work evolved. It is no longer my story, but *their* story from aboard the *USS Virginia*.

The following is a fictionalized account based on the experiences of real people, and which is historically accurate as far as what is known about the voyage of the fleet.

HAMPTON ROADS

On December 12, 1907, sixteen white battleships sailed into view from the Hotel Chamberlin at Hampton Roads. They took their positions as dictated by the line of squadrons for the standard steaming formation consisting of two "parallel lines of eight battleships, anchored with the squadron flagships, *USS Connecticut* and *USS Minnesota* near Old Point Comfort and the mouth of Hampton Roads." (20) To the general supply list were added pies, plum puddings, sacks of walnuts, five-dozen pianos, and fifteen thousand pounds of chocolate bonbons for the *USS Connecticut*. When all the supplies were loaded, the ships sank so low in the water the swells rushed into the open ports and disabled them from firing the row of six- to eight-inch guns. The belts of Krupparmor, (an armor invented by the German Krupp firm to protect a ship from gunfire), usually seen on all ships two feet above the water line were submerged; rendering the entire fleet vulnerable to enemy attack.

WARSHIPS AT ANCHOR IN FRONT OF THE CHAMBERLIN

HOTEL CHAMBERLIN
GEO. F. ADAMS, MGR.
FORTRESS MONROE, VA.

DANCING PAVILION

"The Nations Pride"

13 December 1907

Dear Frank,

I don't know what my free time will be like, but I will do my best to relay information and give you a sense of being here on the *USS Virginia*, as you and Minnie requested in your last letter. I will jot

"Uncle Sam's Personally Conducted Tour of the World."

"That's Going Some."

U. S. BATTLE-SHIP "VIRGINIA"

T-Ville refers to
Tompkinsville, Kentucky

down notes of our cruise as often as I can and then mail them in one envelope.

Hampton Roads, Virginia is our beginning and end for this cruise. I have visited this port many times during the three years of my first tour, but never under any circumstances as historic as this. The number of activities planned before our departure is staggering: receptions, balls, luncheons, football games, baseball games, and rowing matches all ending with a grand ball tonight at the Chamberlin Hotel to honor the officers.

Every day in port, vendors come to our ships selling newspapers and postals. I enclose a card for you, Minnie, of my home, the *USS Virginia*, which will soon take me many miles across the oceans to visit foreign shores I have only read about in books during our T-Ville school days. Of course, that's why I signed on for another tour of duty.

During this busy week of social events, I learned a London Newspaper said a staggering 500 new recruits left their posts. I think that may be an exaggeration but the idea that anyone would abandon their post, especially before such a historical event, is something I can't understand.

Every deserter's possessions are sold at auction, and the money raised pays off any accounts he may have left behind. Word is also sent to the mayor of each deserter's hometown offering a $20 reward for his capture. The reward money, as well as the expenses to bring him back, will be held against his pay. I can honestly say there have been many times when I didn't want to be in this man's navy, but I would never jump ship. You can be sure of that, Frank.

Another change before the onset of our voyage was the removal of Asians who worked as cooks and stewards of the wardrooms. Some of these men have been loyal employees for twenty, even thirty years. They are being replaced by Negro volunteers. Rumor has it these men were removed due to mounting tensions with Japan.

I can't imagine these men are a threat; I found them quite good-natured and hard-working. I heard one Japanese steward was so upset when removed from duty; he tried to drown himself by jumping overboard.

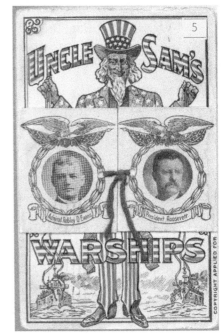

Saturday, 14 December

The weather seems to want to prevent our Monday departure. Fifty miles per hour gale winds have continued throughout the day. Our flagship, the *Connecticut*, was to host a full-dress farewell ball tonight but Admiral Evans has called off the event as well as all shore leave.

Sunday, 15 December

Today dawned with the promise of better weather. With shore leave restriction lifted, men are allowed to go ashore to say final goodbyes to wives and sweethearts. Having no need to do so, I volunteered to help recheck the supplies.

Can you believe each ship is receiving 31 tons of food? Most of the meat we will be eating, however, will be carried on the supply ship, the *Glacier*.

Our diet thus far has been mostly meat and starches, with few fruits and vegetables. Each man receives 1-3/4 pounds of meat a day, which I calculate to be 20,000 pounds served daily.

After going through the inventory list, we discovered some boxes missing. A boat was sent ashore and returned with several crates of Bibles to be distributed to each battleship. (21) I'm sure we'll need them before this cruise is over.

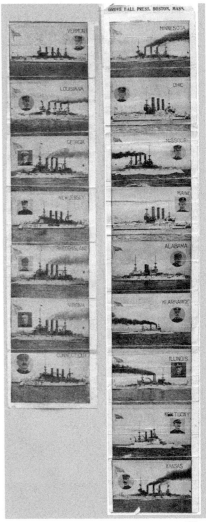

All men are issued a ditty-box, a canvas bag to hold their regulation clothing and a hammock with a leave to secure it to the ceiling at night. A ditty-box is about the size of a bootblack's kit, and holds personal items such as pens, stationery, cigarettes, photos.

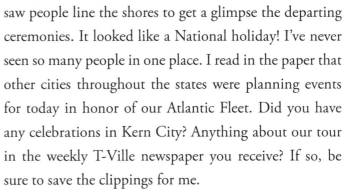

Kern City is now part of Bakersfield

If the weather continues to hold, it looks like we will be leaving on schedule. I've checked my ditty-box making sure I have everything I need for the next few months, especially writing materials. Our first stop is Trinidad, and I don't know if they'll have those items should I run out.

Monday, 16 December

The wind died down, and the sun rose on a crisp, cold morning—a perfect day to begin our voyage. Even before the first light of day, we saw people line the shores to get a glimpse the departing ceremonies. It looked like a National holiday! I've never seen so many people in one place. I read in the paper that other cities throughout the states were planning events for today in honor of our Atlantic Fleet. Did you have any celebrations in Kern City? Anything about our tour in the weekly T-Ville newspaper you receive? If so, be sure to save the clippings for me.

So on to the big event. At 0800, that's 8 am to you landlubbers, all sixteen battleships conducted the ceremony of colors in full dress to honor President Roosevelt aboard his yacht, the *Mayflower*. (It's true. Frank, the President really came and gave us a great send off.) Signal flags, stretching from bow to stern, hung from every masthead. National ensigns were displayed as well. It was an amazing sight.

The commanders of each warship were invited to board the *Mayflower* and have breakfast with the president. We found out later that day that's when the President informed Commander Evans of the complete itinerary for our fleet. We're sailing around the world!

Rumors had speculated about the possibility of a world tour, but confirmation didn't come until that moment. All we officially knew was we were going to San Francisco, after a trip around South America and the Cape.

After the commanders had returned to their posts, we formed into two columns. Then the presidential yacht sailed down the aisle, addressing each ship. When that maneuver was completed, each battleship gave a 21-gun salute, more racket than you can imagine. Then my job began.

The *Mayflower* displayed her signal flags reading "Proceed on your assigned duty." Bands on every ship played the National Anthem while the pennants were dropped and stored in time for the *Connecticut* to signal the first squadron to lift anchor. At precisely 10 am, those eight battleships came about, belching dense clouds of black smoke from their stacks, and headed out to sea.

I wonder if anyone on shore could see what was happening through all the smoke.

The second squadron followed the same pattern. The *Connecticut* led all sixteen ships, passing the crowds in front of the Chamberlin Hotel (I am enclosing a postal of the hotel for your collection, Minnie). As we came close to shore, we could hear onshore bands serenading the fleet with "The Girl I Left Behind" and "Auld Lang Syne." Every time they played "should old acquaintance be forgot," we heard the crowds yell, "No. No. No!"

Our bands on board ship continued to play as well. And, of course, one of the favorite songs was "Home Sweet Home." We played the melody over and over until we couldn't see the shoreline. I thought my lips would give out, they were so numb, but it was

Cartoon (left) from a contemporary newspaper, concerning the fleet's departure from Hampton Roads, Virginia, on 16 December 1907.

President Theodore Roosevelt (at left, with top hat), Uncle Sam and Miss Columbia are shown waving good-bye as the sixteen Atlantic Fleet battleships steam away.

Courtesy of the Naval Historical Foundation, Washington, D.C. Collection of Rear Admiral Harold M. Bemis. U.S. Naval History and Heritage Command Photograph.

worth it to be part of this spectacular send off.

The president preceded the fleet to Horse Shoe —a shoal at the mouth of the Chesapeake Bay— to watch the long column of ships steam past. As a farewell, each ship gave another 21-gun salute as they passed the *Mayflower*.

Between the sixteen ships there are 360 guns ranging from 6 inches to 13 inches bore. A single firing salvo from all guns cost $50,000.

It wasn't until the fleet was several miles out to sea that the president turned his yacht aside.

Each battleship took their assigned position, creating a column at least 3-miles long traveling 400 yards apart. Let me see if I can describe this Frank. I thought with your background as a machinist you'd be interested to know how this distance is maintained.

To maintain the distance of 400 yards while steaming at 10 knots per hour requires constant maintenance using a stadimeter: a modified form of sextant used for finding the distance of an object from its known height, and measures the exact distance from one ship to another within a fraction of an inch.

Each ship weights between 15,000 to 18,000 tons and moves an inch or two faster or slower at the same number of propeller revolutions than the ship before it. The propellers of the same ship operate just slightly different from one another but maintain the same revolutions. It will take time before each ship determines the precise number of revolutions that are necessary to produce the 10 knots of speed and maintain the 400-yard distance. When one ship is off by more than 40 yards, she is required to fly a white triangular pennant with a red border. This action is then counted against the officer of the day. (22)

We have everything we need here, Frank. Every ship is equipped with a machine and carpentry shop, a tailor, shoemaker, a sail making shop for

target practice, a print shop for our newsletter, a sick bay (a place I hope never to visit), and a library as well as one to four new pianos and, of course, the band and orchestra. We play every evening for the men and three times a week for the officers. We also have a drama troupe to help break the monotony of ship life. We have a portable stage shaped to fit in the point of the bow on the main deck, and storerooms full of sets and costumes.

I am not sure you are aware, Frank, but each ship has two companies of Bluejackets forming the infantry and the artillery. Also on board is a company of Marines who perform various special details like the signalmen, pioneers, hospital corps, ammunition party, commissariat (cooks), color guard, buglers and officer's servants. (23) The Marines also form the communication system. They have 98 different bugle calls, which we all have memorized. (24) Newsmen from various magazines have been hand-picked by Roosevelt and, are traveling on some of our ships. There is also an artist, Henry Reuterdahl, sailing on the *Minnesota*. He has cruised with different naval ships for the last nine years. I hope I'm able to meet him on this trip, he's pretty well-known.

I have to tell you I have one of the better jobs in this man's navy. The real workings of a battleship are not so grand and romantic. The Black Gang, the men who work in the belly of the ship, spend most of their time covered in black coal dust as, shovel by shovel, they move coal into the furnaces. One hesitates to take a deep breath down there because the air is so full of coal and ash dust. (25) You also have to hold your ears against the tremendous roar of the boilers. There seems to be very little that can be done to make life easier for those in the Black Gangs. There's little opportunity for them to rest or to come up for fresh air. (26) So, you see, I really do have one of the best jobs here.

Onward and Onward
The Fleet goes round
Wherever you go
Old Glory's now found.

A MINSTRAL SHOW ON BOARD

I'm sure your local newspaper will publish the news of our cruise, probably before you receive this letter. I will have many stories to share when I see you, far more than my letters can hold.

Your friend,

Maurice

22 December 1907

Dear Frank,

Just a quick note

Tomorrow we arrive in Port of Spain, Trinidad. It is hard to believe we've already traveled nearly 1,800 miles. Only three days after leaving Hampton Roads, we received a wireless message from Father Neptune— a warning to prepare for the crossing of the Equator.

Life on the *Virginia* is well, and I never felt better in my life nor had less of this world's possessions! I have the duty in a few minutes so need to close. I am looking forward to seeing you in California, Frank. Do you think Minnie will be able to come with you? You know I would like to see her again. I sure have been thinking about her since you two moved out west.

My best to you and Minnie,

Maurice

During the first two months at sea, twenty-two Black Gang members within the fleet went insane. The *Virginia* reported that every engine room man had lost weight and showed a marked mental change in personality. Many of the men lost chances to go ashore because of their continually dirty appearance which soap and scrubbing seemed to ignore. (27)

TRINIDAD

23 December 1907

Dear Frank,

Sorry it has taken me so long to write. Each ship has a whole lot of young new recruits. It has taken these last few days for the shakedown and to establish routines for the duration of the cruise.

Holiday greetings to you, Frank and Minnie. I hope this letter finds the two of you in good health. I look forward to hearing from you both.

We continued to experience good weather after leaving Hampton Roads keeping us problem free. As we traveled south, it became increasingly warmer, so the daily dress board posted the change in our uniform of the day from blue to white. As we approached the 20th parallel latitude, the Southern Cross came into view in the night sky. What a grand sight to behold. Every evening, when not on duty, we gather on deck and just gaze at the stars.

Four days after leaving Hampton Roads, our problem free cruise ended. On the December 20th, the *Kentucky* had to leave formation

Crux, or the Southern Cross, is visible from the southern hemisphere at nearly any time of year and is frequently used for navigation in much the same way the northern hemisphere uses Polaris, also known as the North Star.

For a few hours every night, in tropical latitudes of the northern hemisphere, the Southern Cross is visible near the horizon during the northern and spring.

Pasachoff, Jay M (2000). Field Guide to the Stars and Planets. Houghton Mifflin Harcourt. p. 67. ISBN 978-0-395-93431-9.

Wash Day

for two hours for repairs. The *Illinois* left formation to take a coal passer with pneumonia to the hospital at the small American-controlled island of Culebra, Puerto Rico. Then the *Missouri* was re-routed to San Juan because a crewman was suffering from peritonitis. Unfortunately, he died before they reached port. That same day, the *Louisiana* suffered an outbreak of diphtheria! Now, didn't I tell you that the *Virginia* was the best ship in the fleet?

Then yesterday, Sunday, December 22, Robert E. Pipes — an ordinary seaman on the *Alabama* — died of spinal meningitis and had to be buried at sea. This was a new experience for me even from a distance. Nothing was known of the death until eight bells sounded at 4 P.M. All the ships raised the national colors. The American flag went up and then slowly came down to half-mast. It felt like the ships themselves stood in reverence. (28) The order was then given for the entire fleet to come to a complete stop. Silence enveloped all the ships when we were told Captain Veeder was reading the short burial service. Pipes' body was sewn in his hammock and weighted down with an iron bar from a furnace grate rather than the usual 24-pound shot as we all stood at attention.

Marines fired three volleys, then all bands played taps as Seaman Pipes slipped into the sea.

The flags again ran up the main mast and down again. The signal was then given for full speed, and we all returned to our duties. The entire service took only a few minutes, yet still weighs heavy on me. Such a ceremony is sobering and makes me truly appreciate family and loved ones the good Lord has provided during our short lives on this earth.

Admiral Evans ordered our speed increased to eleven knots to make up the time lost during the previous two days' troubles, making the 400-yard distance I told you about in my last letter even more difficult to maintain.

Shortly before steaming into the port of Trinidad, the fleet slowed. We spent the day giving our ships a fresh coat of white paint, cleaning the rust from the guns and hulls, waxing our decks to a shine, and polishing the brasswork. We also laid out our clothes on deck, scrubbing them with salt water and soap then hanging them on a line using the stops of eyelet holes on each piece of clothing. (29) Our whites hang above the blue uniforms allowing no 'holidays' on the lines, that's what we call the vacant places. (30) Before reaching Trinidad, every ship's steam laundry used by the officers had broken down. The officers had to hand wash and hang their uniforms with ours. It helps them understand our lot on the ship, don't you think?

With clean uniforms and freshly painted ships, we were ready to steam into port. The first two thousand men were chosen to go on shore leave based on their merits and good behavior. Almost all men who had reached the rank of first class received shore leave to represent America to a foreign country. As you might remember, I was promoted to first class as an incentive to sign up for a second tour of duty. The officers only chose men who resembled "the all-American red-apple cheeked man" and not one member of the Black Gang nor those with facial or skin disorders, were chosen. We have so many young recruits with facial breakouts that were not selected.

I was fortunate— though I don't consider myself a red-apple cheeked man — because of my rank. After receiving our pay, every man was ordered to have their hair cut, take a quick bath using buckets of water on deck, and to study the library's etiquette books to be prepared for the correct behavior when on shore. We could have taken a real bath as new shower baths have been installed. But the water is piped

COALING SHIP FROM A COLLIER

Without the release of a few beers that many sailors had grown accustomed to, a few men turned to wood alcohol, accidentally ending their lives.

directly into the boilers making the water scalding hot. The officers even instructed us on the proper way to use toothpicks that had been on the mandatory supply list for each ship. One wonders where most of these men have come from!

I found it interesting, Frank, that while we were drilled on the proper behavior for shore leave, the officers were also drilled on the correct depth for bows and the proper placement of hands when waltzing with wives of dignitaries. They were told 'always wear a smile' and of course be charming. The life of a Bluejacket for me!

A Shore Patrol was created before we dropped anchor, to further ensure good behavior and to leave a positive impression at foreign ports. The patrol consists of eight officers: four commissioned, four midshipmen, and two men from each ship of the division. Leave ends at 8:00 pm each evening. Shore Patrol begins their round up at 7:00 pm, and there is a new rule. During this good-will cruise, drunkenness and carousing will not be tolerated, which is fine by me. We were told the slightest offender will be placed in iron shackles and kept several days on bread and water. You can see why everyone wants a 'C & S' (Clean and Sober) inscribed next to his name when coming back aboard after his leave. (31)

Even though we've been pent up for a while, me and my buddies are more interested in seeing the sights, hunting for post-cards and camera film when we go ashore. I'm determined to find the most interesting postals for Minnie's collection.

Every morning while in the port, those ships not coaling grant their men shore leave. And every morning, the Patrol is to report to the flagship with their handcuffs to receive their orders. The ranking officer of the patrol will stay at the police headquarters of the country while the others roam the favorite known haunts of the sailors. (32) It will be interesting to see how all this plays out.

After our final inspection and the drilling concerning shore leave completed, we gathered speed, ready to enter the Dragon's

IN THE SUBURBS OF TRINIDAD CHRISTMAS DAY 1908.

Mouth, which is a series of straits separating the Gulf of Paria from the Caribbean Sea.

We arrived in Trinidad today, just after sunset expecting a huge welcome. What a disappointment! After all of our preparation for this port, our new white paint and polished decks, not one soul greeted us from shore. American ships have always been welcomed here with parties, dances, and receptions. Trinidad is under British rule, so maybe England is not thrilled with the idea of an American battleship fleet going around the world before they do. Rumor is spreading that England instructed Governor Jackson of Trinidad to do only what was absolutely necessary for us. The governor even called off the Governor's Ball and canceled all the usual entertainment that the private citizens always finance.

26 December

Merry Christmas, dear friends. I hope you and Minnie had a nice Holiday.

Interesting time here, Frank. We waited a full day after we dropped anchor for the Royal Navy launch to arrive and officially greet the *Connecticut* so that those men who were on board ships not involved in the coaling process could go ashore. They reported the Governor was ill and if Admiral Evans would like to come ashore and take a hotel room, the Governor would be happy to see him.

Did I mention earlier that Admiral Evans limps from a war injury? Well, it seems his leg has become quite painful, and he had to be helped by Admirals Sperry, Thomas, and Emory. When the Admirals came ashore, there was only a small musical band to greet them. Indeed, we are not impressed with our welcome in Trinidad.

The reporters on board the ships knew their followers back home did not want to read about the unwelcome reception. The stories submitted were colored to give the impression Trinidad indeed had treated the American Navy with the respect they felt they deserved. However, many were concerned this cold welcome was Britain's way of showing their further alliance with Japan. Robert Dunn, the special correspondent aboard the *Rhode Island*, expressed the feelings of the men very well when he wrote, Trinidad "Respects Yankee fleet no more than a squadron of tramps and luggers. (33)

Christmas wasn't too bad out here in the tropics, Frank. In many ways it was a happy one, but in it was also a sad day to be so far from home. On this day above all others, my thoughts travel homeward, more so than any other time. (34)

As soon as we arrived in Trinidad, we began decorating our ship for the holiday. We gathered greenery from the shore and added it to what we had brought from Hampton Roads. Christmas Eve, we decorated the cabin doors with wreaths and draped palm branches over the railings. We made signs that read "Peace on Earth, Good Will to Men," and suspended them from the guns of the main turrets. Interesting place to hang such a sign, don't you think?

Christmas afternoon was filled with boat races and baseball games. A holiday dinner of roast turkey, ham, gravy, dressing, mashed potatoes, cranberries, mince pie, plum pudding, coffee, and cigars was served on tables decorated with spruce Christmas trees. I enjoyed playing holiday music on deck while the men entertained themselves either waltzing with each other or singing. There was even a group of officers from the *Louisiana* who rowed by each ship singing Christmas Carols and playing mandolins. All in all, a good Christmas was had by all.

Only one official dinner was held for the rear admirals and captains. After the dinner, the officers returned to their ships. There wasn't one speech or toast during the entire evening.

Our main reason to stop in Trinidad was to take on supplies and to re-coal our ships after our 1,800-mile journey. Because the *Virginia* is in the Second Division, we are one of the first ships to take on coal. The amount of coal we use is measured every 24 hours, written down, and announced to the ships. We have developed a contest between all of us to see which vessel can use the least amount of fuel. Even with the competition, the sixteen battleships and the auxiliaries combined still

use about 1,500 tons of coal a day while cruising. When in port, we average about twenty-five tons of coal a day.

The coaling procedure began on Christmas Eve, the day after we arrived. We were glad coaling was suspended for Christmas day to give us a holiday feeling. The First Division coaled first, one division coals at a time. As I mentioned before, if a ship is not coaling, shore leave is granted. It was four days before the job was completed. Everyone, including the officers, has a part in the re-coaling process.

Coaling is considered a drill. In times of war, speed is essential. Dress regulations are always lifted, which allows for some pretty wild outfits. Some men wear worn-out uniforms, civilian hats, or loud ties. One fellow even wore a top hat while coaling, which unfortunately he lost to the sea. My job, when not actively engaged in coaling, is to keep the music going. The men particularly like ragtime music played from the bridge. It seems to help them work better and maintain a steady speed.

Coaling is a dirty, yet fascinating process. We first sand the deck so the coal dust will mingle with the sand and not grime up the woodwork. Then cranes lift sacks of ashes out of the hold of the ship and place them in lighters. When not in a foreign port, we dump the ashes in the sea, which saves us a good bit of time.

Lighter: "A vessel, commonly an unpowered, flat-bottomed barge, used in lightening, unloading ships, or in transporting goods for short distances." (35)

After the hold is cleared out, the First Division ties up alongside the waiting colliers. Shovelers from each ship go aboard the colliers and into the hot, humid holds to begin their work. The maximum time a man can stay in the hold is 30 minutes before a new shift comes aboard. We keep buckets of cold water ready for the men when they climb out of the hold. You should see them — black with only the whites of their eyes showing, coughing up coal dust and dripping with sweat. I have included a postcard so you can get an idea of what I'm talking about.

When the shovelers have filled an 800-pound sack, the derrick hoist lifts it to the main deck and drags it to the nearby coal chutes. The coalmen then dump the bags of coal into the bunkers.

Because this is Trinidad's hottest time of year, it became quite a hindrance to us. Due to the heat, the coal had to be rushed doubly fast to the bunkers to keep it from igniting in transit. Even the pitch in the seams of the decks became unbearably hot.

There is competition between individual ships as well as within each division during coaling. A good crew, which of course we are, can handle around 100 tons of coal an hour. Every hour a signal is given from the yardarm to change the configuration of the flags to indicate the total number tons taken aboard.

The air becomes thick with coal dust penetrating all parts of the ship and every part of our bodies. The last ship to coal was the *Maine*, we all know it's the greatest coal eater of the fleet, so it took the longest to re-coal. (36) When the bunkers were filled, and the colliers had departed, we had a navy 'field day' to clean the ship again. It took us the remainder of our stay in Trinidad to do a complete scrub down to ready our ship for sailing.

When I took my shore leave after we coaled and cleaned up the ship, I looked the place over and came back to the ship early. Shops were closed, streets deserted, and the people we did encounter treated us coldly. Only about half of the merchants flew American flags above their shops, and only about fifty people came down to view the ships. The only visitors who seemed to have an interest in the fleet were the fruit vendors, especially the alligator pear men, and the merchants who had things to sell, like Panama hats and parrots. (37)

Rumors circulated around Trinidad saying that American sailors carried big knives to carve up everything and everybody. It's no wonder merchants closed their shops and people hid from us. It angered me that people would believe such rumors. The few stores that remained open charged double for their merchandise. Nevertheless, I did purchase a few post-cards for Minnie, which I enclose.

Some of the men stayed in town to ride the American trolley cars or play baseball in a park at the center of town. I preferred to go back to the ship.

Alligator Pear is another the term for Avocado

Frank, I can't believe the new recruits. These men are bringing back a menagerie! As I sit on deck writing this letter, I saw a couple of men boarding with parrots and monkeys. We already have quite a collection of dogs and goats traveling with us. It will be interesting to see how they all get along.

I must close this letter as it's time for our evening concert.

Please give Minnie my best.

Maurice

"Men bought postal cards by the thousands." (38)

30 December

Dear Frank and Minnie,

We completed the coaling and re-scrubbing yesterday morning, so we left Trinidad in the afternoon headed for Brazil. As far as I'm concerned, we couldn't leave soon enough. We were all happy to be on our way after the welcome we received. Trinidad just isn't fit for Americans. Out of the thirty thousand people who populate this place, the large majority are blacks. (39) This is not a place I care to return.

It's time for our evening concert for the officers, so I will close with best wishes for the New Year.

Maurice

During the coaling process in Trinidad, one of the men on the *Ohio* found a half stick of dynamite wrapped in paraffin to keep it dry. Orders went to every ship to watch each piece of coal for the other half of dynamite. Sabotage was always a concern of all navies, and rumors had circulated regarding just such an event. For the next fourteen months, the over-worked Black Gangs had to search lump by lump through thousands of tons of coal before sending it to the boiler. The second half of the dynamite stick was never found. The only men who knew of this impending danger were the highest officers and the coalmen. The dynamite could have been placed on ship by anyone. Civilians came aboard all the time for tours, dances and dinners.

BATTLESHIP VIRGINIA, Capt. Seaton Schroeder; tonnage 14,948; keel laid 1902; cost $3,590,000; 435 feet long; 76 feet wide; 812 men and officers; 24 guns.

COPYRIGHTED BY F. MULLER

8 January 1908

Dear Frank and Minnie,

New Year's Eve arrived two days out from Trinidad, giving us a break in our routine. To celebrate, the smoking lamp was lit all day. We paraded around in pirate and Indian costumes singing and banging on tubs while sirens screeched and beams of light shown from all the ships. Through the wireless, we learned on another ship the Bluejackets played practical jokes on the officers by staging a mutiny. On another, some of the officers spent the night serenading the men and commanding officers alike, keeping everyone awake. However, all during the New Year's celebration, every ship continued steaming in squadron formation, two lines of battleships, with the supply ships, or beef ships, bringing up the rear midway between the lines. (40)

With the festivities we began to relax, thinking it would be routine sailing to our next port of call. It was not to be. There were a series of breakdowns along the coast of Brazil, slowing our schedule. Sometimes, Admiral Evans received four or five distress calls in one day. He blamed the complications on carelessness by the officer of the day. He sent the guilty ships to the *observation ward*, a position of shame between the two columns of ships. (41)

The seas were a bit rocky, which increased our coal consumption, slowing our pace to 9 or 10 knots. On top of these problems, there was a miscalculation of the sailing distance from Trinidad to Rio. Instead of 2,900 miles as listed on the charts, it was actually 3,300 miles. Because of this error, the *New Jersey* found she was going to be short 80 tons of coal. Evans shifted her to the rear of the division allowing her to sail at a slower speed. Even with the change of position, we were sure she'd run out of coal about two hours before reaching Rio and have to be towed. Not a good showing for the United States to arrive in port towing one of our proud ships.

The *Illinois* and the *Alabama* have the smallest capacity for coal of our fleet. The *Illinois* carries 700 tons less than the *New Jersey*. So, with the *New Jersey* in trouble and the miscalculation of mileage, we all had to cut down on our consumption of fuel. Freshwater bathing was forbidden and the use of electric lights restricted.

We were seventeen hours behind schedule on 3 January when the *Maine* began to run out of coal and started begging the other ships to share their supply. Admiral Evans refused to stop again, further delaying our arrival time. The *Maine* devours a third more coal than the other ships when steaming at regulation speed. Now you know why we call her, the greatest coal eater of the fleet. The *Maine* always seems to be covered with black soot gushing down the sides of her hull after a rainstorm because of all the extra sacks of coal stacked on her decks. With all of her problems, she's been condemned to the observation ward more than any other ship. If I were Evans, the *Maine* would be quite an embarrassment. I'd think about sending her home.

To add to our problems, the next night we observed four white ardois lanterns fluttering at the masthead of the *Missouri*. These were followed by three rapid signals from the red light at the top of the masthead spelling out 'Z,' which means 'Man overboard'. The entire fleet stopped and turned their searchlights to the sea to search for this man. As a beacon to the lost sailor, the *Missouri* hurled copper life-buoys containing cans of calcium chloride overboard. They immediately burst into flame when they hit the water.

Next, the *Missouri* lowered a lifeboat. The *Kentucky* also lowered a lifeboat. Six oarsmen and a coxswain manned each boat. In the stern of each lifeboat are kept enough fresh water and provisions for two days.

Frank, there are six things that have to be accomplished when a man is thought to be overboard:

1. Flash "Z" on the ardois red light,
2. Steer the ship out of the column,
3. Stop the engines and change the white truck-light to announce the ship is steaming at cruise speed to a red light, which means the ship has stopped its engines. (If the red light begins to blink it means the ship is backing up.)
4. Fire a gun,
5. Drop the life buoys, and
6. Lower a lifeboat.

The searchlights continued to circle the waters, and the lifeboats wandered around aimlessly. There was no sign of life. After several hours, the *Missouri*'s ardois lit up again flashing a long message. It seems a seaman had been sleeping in the side hammock had a nightmare and called out, "Man overboard!" This little episode caused us to lose yet another half day from our schedule.

We heard later on the wireless men were laughing about the *Connecticut's* admiral. It seems he was abruptly rousted out of his bed during all this commotion. Coatless and still in slippers, he hurried out of his cabin, but not before he grabbed a stogie, bit the end off and put it into his mouth. Reports say that he went to each officer from the flag lieutenant to the quartermaster to the yeoman to the signalman, and everyone in between, asking for a light! (42) You can sure see what mattered to this officer!

9 January

Sunday, 5 January, all hands were called on deck for general muster. King Neptune and his slaves came aboard and were greeted with the blare of trumpets. A messenger of his court carried a large leather pouch containing a subpoena for each man who had not crossed the line and been granted permission to enter His Majesty's domain. Enclosed is a copy my buddy received for the initiation into the King Neptune's domain (43) so you can see what we are up against each time we cross the Equator.

Domain of His Majesty, Neptunus Rex, Equatorial Region,

January 4, 1908

To Michael T. Nolan, Musician Second Class, United States Navy, Greeting:

Being a Landlubber and daring to enter Our Aqueous and Equatorial Regions without due and submissive ceremony, you are hereby ordered and directed to appear in person before My Most August Presence in Latitude 0' 00' 00", Longitude 37" West, on January 5, 1908, to explain your most contumacious conduct, and to accept most heartily and with good grace the pains and penalties of the Awful Tortures that will be inflicted upon you, to the end that you may become an honorable Shellback.

Signed: NEPTUNUS REX. (44)

Once the invitations were delivered, King Neptune assured the captain he was protected because of his previous travels. King Neptune announced he and his court would visit the ship at 1:30 pm tomorrow. The messengers quickly left our ship accompanied again by a blare of our trumpets.

That night we crossed the equator around midnight. Each ship placed only those men on watch who had encountered King Neptune before and were considered honorable shellbacks. For the first time, I was grateful to pull the duty. Those unfortunates who received the subpoenas from His Majesty slept very little that night. I am sure they dreamt about the awful tortures awaiting them the following day. I have to tell you, Frank, I'm very glad to be on the other side of this, once is quite enough for me.

Since 19 December, mysterious messages had popped up at the *scuttlebutt*, drinking water station, detailing the terrible things that would happen to the men when we crossed the line. One of the messages detailed items each ship received while in Trinidad: 750 gallons of coal tar, 90 gallons of varnish, 400 pounds of sulfur, 4 sets of razors complete, 18 brushes, 4 sets of fine rib saws, 4 surgical knives, 2 large meat axes and 15 pairs of handcuffs. (45) Another message issued to the King's doctors to have their pills and gargle water ready, another to the barbers to mix a lather of coal tar, oil, molasses and India ink. (46)

Frank, this ceremony is difficult to explain. Unless you witness this first hand, it's difficult to grasp the full impact. But I will to try to draw you a picture as best I can because I think you and Min will get a real kick out of the elaborate proceedings.

All during this ceremony, I was seated with our band playing "Columbia, the Gem of the Ocean." This gave me an excellent view of the proceedings. During breaks, I was able to take some fine photos, which I will make into postals and enclose them in a letter.

King Neptune and his slaves came aboard the *Virginia*, at 1:30 pm as promised, dressed in an odd assortment of clothes—long wigs, tall hats, clown shoes, and big webbed frog feet. The story goes like this: at one time the slaves were human, but due to some unknown transgressions toward the King, they became weird creatures. Even Captain Schroeder bowed to the court of Neptune, for the King and his court became the rulers of our ship as soon as they came aboard.

King Neptune's wife, Amphitrite, his secretary, two barbers, a squad of policemen, and the bearers of his royal carriage accompanied him. Two doctors, Dr. Flip and Dr. Flap, boarded the *Virginia* carrying suitcases filled with saws, knives, teeth extractors, and several bottles of smelly medicines. Dr. Flip told the ship's surgeon "I'm from the old school and a graduate of the Royal College of the Doldrums, class of Umpdy-umpdy-umpump." (47)

A large tarp was gathered at its ends then suspended on four sides to form a tank as ordered by King Neptune. Once completed, Dr. Flip presented the prescription with which to fill the tank:

Crossing the line, January 1st—the Initiation.

"Black Molasses, two barrels.
Coal Tar, five buckets,
Dissolved Glue, one bucket.
Mix with sufficient bilge water to a depth to permit immersion" (48)

On a platform overlooking the swimming tank, were placed four barbers' chairs with their backs to the newly formed bath. The royal police brought four landlubbers before His Majesty and asked them to explain why they dared to appear in this region without permission of the King. Each man was placed in a barber chair, lathered with grease

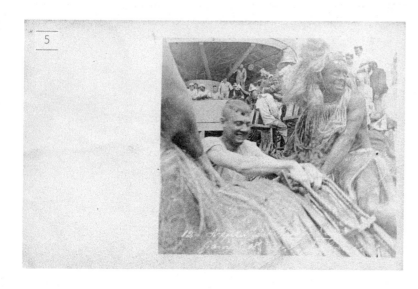

mixed with white lead and then shaved with a dull razor. Then these men were forced to swallow a pill of soap and cayenne pepper the size of a nutmeg. (49)

Once this part of the initiation was complete, they pulled the levers on the barber chairs, and the four men slid into the water tank where the servants of His Majesty waited. They filled the mouths of these four men with tar and shampooed their heads with molasses. The louder a man protested, the longer his treatment. Running deck hoses, sand, and canvas were kept nearby to help scrub the men when they emerged. After the first four landlubbers had received their initiation, four more were presented. Officers and enlisted men alike were given the same treatment unless they chose to pay the fine of one barrel of beer in lieu of the soap pill and Turkish bath. However, to become real shellback, one must take the initiation in the usual way. No one on our ship chose to pay the fine. After the initiation, each man received an individualized lithograph certificate:

DOMAIN OF NEPTUNUS REX, RULER OF THE RAGING MAIN

To all Sailors, wherever ye may be, and to all Mermaids, Sea Serpents, Whales, Sharks, Porpoises, Dolphins, Skates, Eels Suckers, Lobsters, Crabs, Pollywogs, and other living things of the sea, Greetings:

Know ye that on this 6th day of January 1908, in latitude 0 00', longitude 37, 11' degrees West, there appeared within the limits of Our Royal Domain the United States ship *VIRGINIA*, bound southward from the Strait of Magellan and Pacific ports. Be it remembered that the said vessel and Officers and crew thereof have been inspected and passed by Ourselves and Our Royal Staff;

And be it known by all the Sailors, Marines, Landlubbers, and others who may be honored by his presence, that MICHAEL T.

NOLAN, U.S.N., having been found worthy to be numbered as one of our trusty Shellbacks, has been gathered to our fold and duly initiated into the Ancient Order of the Deep.

Be it further understood that by virtue of the power invested in me, I do hereby command all my subjects to show due honor and respect to him whenever he may enter our realm. Disobey this order under penalty of royal displeasure.

Given under our hand and seal this sixth day of January 1908.

(Signed) NEPTUNUS REX (50)

"I GOT MINE"~ CROSSING THE EQUATOR

It was a great day for all except the Black Gang in the furnace room and the midshipmen who had command of the bridge and the task of keeping us on course.

I hope this letter finds you and Minnie well and gives you an idea of my life aboard the *Virginia*. Keep taking those pictures, Frank. I hope you can give me some pointers when we get together. I am just beginning to get acquainted with my new camera.

Your friend, Maurice

The captains wanted to maintain a happy, positive attitude on board and the newspapermen wanted stories for their readers. The newsmen wrote about every football game, horseplay, ice cream party, songfest, and minstrel show. The crossing of the equator filled over 20 columns in the *New York Sun* alone. (51) Between the sixteen ships, around 450 officers and over 10,000 enlisted men became a shellbacks. This kind of reporting, and also the better recreational activities on board ship, were a new tactic for public relations and future recruiting.

RIO DE JANEIRO

13 January 1908

Dear Frank and Minnie,

Well, we never made up the time lost at sea. The fleet entered the Rio harbor Sunday, 12 January, two days behind schedule, dropping anchor in four parallel lines in front of the beach at 4:00 pm. You wouldn't believe the crowd that greeted us. Those people must have spent months getting ready for our arrival. There were twelve Brazilian cruisers and a hundred small vessels crowding the harbor along with thousands of spectators on the shore waving flags and hats to welcome us. What an incredible sight after our disappointment in Trinidad.

Each battleship issued a 21-gun salute to honor Brazil's president. We are instructed to issue the salute to presidents of all countries when we drop anchor. After the sun set, we prepared our own special welcome for Rio. All the battleships turned on their searchlights and hung green and yellow lights along the deck rails and around the guns. What a colorful sight. The Brazilians answered back with a display of fireworks from the hilltops. This event began the celebration in Rio.

We weren't able to go ashore until this morning. The reliable men were assembled, given the usual chatter about our expected behavior and ferried to shore. (Yes, Frank, I am still one of the "reliable men!")

When we reached the town, we located the ferry building that had been set up to help us become orientated to the city. What a blessing that was! It was easy to spot the building with the sign on the outside, "Information Bureau for the American Seamen." Inside, the counters were manned with attendants to answer all of our questions. There were postal card booths, a booth to exchange money, and a booth to sell tickets for various events. (52) There were also writing areas set aside with free paper and envelopes, as you can see by this letter. I purchased some of the postcards at this Bureau, and others at emporiums around the city. Let me know, Min, if you find these to your liking.

Let me clarify a story that circulated throughout the fleet and probably will hit some of the newspapers in the States. As usual, some of the men headed for the saloons as soon as they reached the shore instead of crowding the post card emporiums like me and my buddies. (54) Two of the sailors who had opted for a saloon sat down and ordered beer. While seated at the bar, they watched a fight between two Rio men grow out of hand. A bottle was thrown, which missed its mark and struck one of our sailors, who immediately jumped into the fight. The Rio men were ushered out of the bar returning to the saloon with knives.

The troublemakers were kicked out of the saloon a second time. A few minutes later they returned with reinforcements. Meanwhile, the sailors also rounded up reinforcements. The Shore Patrol, cruising around town in rented automobiles, spotted the trouble and got into the act against the Brazilians. A crowd of at least 1,000 people gathered to observe the fight.

Then the Brazilian police showed up, adding to the confusion. As the story goes, one policeman picked up a rock and threw it at a Bluejacket while another policeman began beating on a sailor. The policemen drew their swords, inflicting stab wounds on several of the

During the time the fleet stayed in Rio, the bureau estimated the Americans had used 8,000 sheets of paper and 5,000 envelopes. The men and the officers purchased 21,000 guide pamphlets to the city, 175,000 postal stamps, and about 170,000 postcards. (53)

Shore Patrol and one seaman. This ruckus was not the fault of our men but, of course, Admiral Evans suspended all shore leave to investigate the matter. We should hear the outcome soon.

16 January

Well Frank, as luck would have it, on 14 January the governor of Rio came out to the *Connecticut* the next morning to give his apologies. Lucky for us, after the governor left, Evans reinstated our shore leave. (55) I haven't heard about the injured men, only that they are aboard ship recovering.

With shore leave reinstated, the celebrations continued. There were ice cream socials, sightseeing tours in American trolley cars, (56) athletic events, and band concerts.

AMERICAN SAILORS ASHORE AT RIO DE JENERIO, BRAZIL, JAN. 15, 1908.

One of my duties is to perform with our band at many of the onshore functions, providing the entertainment. This allows me to attend events I wouldn't be allowed to as an enlisted man. It's not hard duty, but very tiring, and sometimes quite boring to hear the same speeches over and over again. I'm not sure I could endure what these officers have to in the name of "good relations" with our foreign neighbors. Just to give you an idea of what I'm talking about, an officer's typical day of celebrations in Rio went something like this:

- Breakfast: Admiral Thomas gives a speech because Admiral Evans could not attend

- View and present the trophy to the winning team of the rowing races or other athletic events of the day

- Attend a special mass at the Cathedral for the safety of the fleet

- Luncheon atop Mt. Corcovado requiring a long dizzy cable ride

- A garden party

- Sightseeing tour

- Reception at an exclusive club or Botanical Garden

- Another banquet and a speech by Admiral Thomas,

- and finally, at the end of the day, an opera, dance or a grand ball at the Crystal Palace.

Most of the officers I talked to were becoming physically exhausted from the endless schedule of events. But you know, we grew weary as well as our bandmaster forever struggling through the bars of the Brazilian national hymn. (57) That hymn is so long, that when we serenaded a Brazilian ship heading out to sea, the ship was out of hearing distance long before we completed the song. Much to my relief, our bandmaster instructed us to shorten it so we could save our lips and our wind. I wonder if he didn't shorten the hymn because our director always complained we could not play it properly due to most our new members came from the mid-west. (58) The rhythms *were* difficult to play, but protocol states the hospitality the fleet receives must be reciprocated; that includes playing their national anthem.

If you noticed, I said Admiral Thomas gave the speeches. By the time we arrived in Rio, Admiral Evans was quite sick with gout. He stayed very close to his bed. The senior officer, Rear Admiral Charles M. Thomas took over the job of attending the social obligations, though he doesn't look all that healthy himself, and Admiral Robert Ingersoll carried out the high-ranking decisions.

Every afternoon around 4:00 pm, I saw beautiful, over-dressed, powdered women wearing the latest fashions and fabrics— probably from Paris, Min — riding around in fancy carriages. They put on quite a show for the Brazilian men as well as for us. We stationed ourselves in strategic spots around the café tables on the Avenida Central to watch, sipping black coffee. But I found their coffee just too strong to tolerate; it is thick like syrup. I much prefer the lemonade. But you might have enjoyed it, Frank. Especially while viewing the pretty ladies!

21 January

With the job of coaling complete, the *Minnesota* gave a gala reception this afternoon and a ball aboard ship to end our stay. Henry Reuterdahl, the artist I mentioned in one of my first letters, was in charge of the decorations. We all thought he was just an artist but have since learned he is secretly a news correspondent for the unauthorized magazine, *McClures*.

There are quite a few men who are not pleased to have that man aboard their ship. He wrote an article for his magazine before we sailed from Hampton Roads criticizing the age of our commanding officers and the promotional system of the Navy. He also criticized the battleships themselves regarding the waterline armor riding too low in the water because of all the supplies we had taken on. Well, I suppose he did have a point, but I don't think our Navy needs any more criticism and certainly not publicly.

Anyway, with Reuterdahl's talent, he sure did the *Minnesota* up fine. He did get a little carried away with his decorations, and spent more than the allotted amount for the event. So much was said about the spectacular display, I went over to see for myself. He put up garlands of roses, potted plants, and flags to hide the guns in the turrets. He even built a rock garden with a miniature waterfall and a pool for goldfish under the guns. Two bands played for dancing on the aft and fore decks, and

Two political factions were brewing when the fleet arrived: those who favored President Penna of Brazil and those who opposed him. This tension produced a charged atmosphere. The anti-Penna party refused to attend any function to which the Americans had been invited. They also refused to wash our officers' uniforms in protest of what they thought was America's support of President Penna. Evans received a telegram from Washington saying the terrorists of the anti-Penna party might try to call attention to their cause by damaging his ships.

Sailor Boys Reading Letters from Home.

tables were loaded with sandwiches and a non-alcoholic punch. They say over 3,000 civilians attended this reception.

22 January

Dear Frank,

This letter will be my last until after we are well out to sea.

Today is another blistering hot day in Rio. It is so warm that by 10:00 am, the seams in the deck of our ship were exuding pitch. (59) But I didn't even notice the heat for the mail arrived from the States for the first time since leaving Hampton Roads—at least twenty bags of mail for each ship!

It is so good to hear from the both of you and to learn that you two will be making the trip to Los Angeles to view the fleet. Thank you, Frank, for your letter and the December T-Ville newspaper. It felt good to hold a piece of home. Frank, Minnie said she is looking forward to seeing the fleet of ships up close, but did she say anything to you about seeing one particular sailor up close?

I'd forgotten you have an aunt living in Santa Ana, so you'll be able to spend time with her and afford yourselves a place to stay. I was amazed, but not too surprised, to learn that the large paper in Hopkinsville, Kentucky, printed only one line about this cruise on 17 December: "Admiral Evans' fleet has sailed from Hampton Roads for the Pacific." I assume that means there wasn't much of a celebration after all in my hometown.

It won't be long now before we get together again. I am looking forward to being on American soil. I want to answer Minnie's letter and prepare her postals to mail.

Your friend,

Maurice

Reckner in his book, *Teddy Roosevelt's Great White Fleet*, pointed out that Brazil was most gracious to the Americans because the United States was the biggest importer of their coffee, whereas the other South American countries had their alliances with Europe. However, Hart states in his book, *The Great White Fleet*, Brazil was not usually this friendly toward Americans and thought of them as barbarians. He felt the fleet was being used as a token. Brazil had ordered a battleship from England in the early part of 1908. Hart felt Brazil had used the Atlantic Fleet to demonstrate to its people the importance of having their own fleet of battleships.

Maurice after reading Frank's letter wrote a short note to Minnie on the back of one of her postcards, "Your valued letter has smoothed off the corners of my entire system. And I am quite sure if I am so lucky to continue in your good graces I will be a better man when I again meet you."

Because of the dynamite incident in Trinidad, Admiral Evans ordered all the civilians to be screened when they boarded the ships. But with so many people attending the reception on the *Minnesota*, it was impossible to check everyone. Not only was Evans concerned about terrorists of the anti-Penna party, but he had heard rumors about Russian and Japanese spies trailing the fleet. There were reports from Canada warning Evans against Japanese sabotage. Each night while in port, small boats with searchlights continually scanned the waters around the ships for protection. The officers were instructed to keep all of this information under wraps. There was no dynamite found in Rio. It is interesting to note, however, that after the cruise, Admiral Sperry confided to a friend that dynamite and other explosives were found in the coal of different ships at various ports. (60)

At the end of the ten-day visit, President Penna sent a note to President Roosevelt complimenting him on the American Fleet and on the conduct of the men while ashore. The message President Roosevelt sent back to Brazil was published in the Brazilian newspapers. This note was interpreted as a treaty alliance claiming Brazil as the most powerful country in South America, thus infuriating her other South American neighbors.

PUNTA ARENAS, CHILE (SANDY POINT)

The Atlantic Fleet passing through the Straits of Magellan.
February 8, 1908.

2574

Eleven Latin American countries sent invitations to President Roosevelt inviting the fleet for a review, but he selected only Brazil and Peru to be visited with full honors. The Navy added Punta Arenas, Chile, and Magdalena Bay, Mexico for coaling stops. Argentina, in competition with Brazil, was not pleased to hear of the fleet's visit to Rio de Janeiro but her harbor was too shallow for the battleships. To pacify Argentina, the six torpedo destroyers were sent for a visit. Uruguay also became upset when the fleet passed them by and promptly ordered their first battleship.

8 February 1908

Dear Frank and Minnie,

The band doesn't have to perform this evening. The smoking lights have been turned on, and the waters are relatively calm, so I finally have some time to sit a spell, take out my writing tools and bring you up to date by going through the pages of my journal.

After receiving the first mail from home on 22 January, we set sail for Chile. At 3:30 pm, the usual 21-gun salute was given, and a presidential review followed. Thousands of Brazilians packed the shoreline to say good-bye to us despite a heavy downpour of rain. The entire Brazilian Navy, embarking on a cruise to train their midshipmen, followed our vessels out to sea. It was a tremendous send-off.

On the cold, foggy day of 27 January, we spotted several Argentinean cruisers bearing down on the fleet with bands playing and guns saluting. This action was no surprise to the officers, as this meeting was apparently pre-planned before we left Rio. Sixty-four times they played the "Star Spangled Banner" while the cruisers steamed passed our fleet. They displayed their fancy maneuvers giving us an unexpected naval pageant on the high seas. It was a welcomed interruption to our routine.

The next challenge we faced before reaching Chile was the treacherous waters of the Straits of Magellan. The Straits are a 360-mile long natural passage between the Atlantic and Pacific oceans. The width varies from one and a half miles to twenty-five miles. If you look on a map, you'll see the straits are V-shaped, with the narrow end reaching into the Atlantic and the wider end opening into the Pacific.

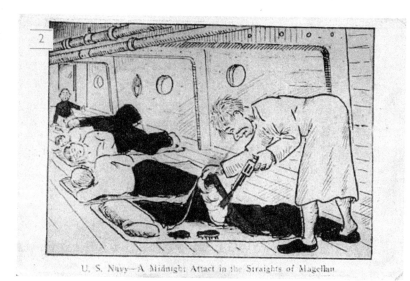

U. S. Navy—A Midnight Attack in the Straights of Magellan

The entrance of the straits is marked by high cliffs on each side and thick fog hiding the submerged rocks. All along the straits are whirlpools, unpredictable currents, heavy tides, and giant squalls. The hurricane-type wind that comes down from the mountains into the sea making a huge roar, called williwaws, have the reputation of lifting ships clear out of the water. One moment you feel the sea is calm and the next minute your ship is tossed about by churned-up waters. It feels like you're being torn to pieces. (61) We can't even trust the buoys in this area because we've been told they may have been rearranged by crooks, hoping to rob lost ships. This area has been aptly nicknamed by previous sailors,

Delusion Bay, Desolation Island, Point Famine, Point Mercy, Useless Bay, and Dislocation Point.

As we entered the straits, the thermometer dropped. We changed our uniforms back to our warmer blue wool, had to wear our overcoats, and used blankets at night. After the stifling heat of the equator, we welcomed the cool breezes along the straits.

Muelle de Carga, Punta Arenas (Magallanes) 1910

We arrived in Punta Arenas, Chile, the world's southernmost city, on 1 February. Punta Arenas has a deep-water harbor, making it an excellent port for re-coaling, which was our primary objective.

The town has a reputation for being the most depressing and barren place in the world. To my eyes, it was a very desolate looking city as we dropped anchor. Although this city holds a population smaller than the total number of our ships, we were met by thousands of greeters lining the beaches. The Chilean Government, however, did very little to provide us with entertainment. Perhaps this stemmed from the many spies who reportedly arrived ahead of the fleet. Before we dropped anchor, a Russian spy, who'd attempted to come aboard at Hampton Roads and Rio, surfaced again in Chile. I also heard there were two Japanese spies with binoculars who were spotted keeping a close eye on the fleet.

When I went ashore, I noticed that nearly all the merchants in town had freshly painted signs over their businesses which read: "Special Prices to the American fleet." They had special prices all right; the cost of their merchandise had doubled since our arrival. It was also clear the town possessed a great deal of wealth.

Despite the barren landscape, fancy carriages toured wealthy women all around town. Their heads were covered with mantillas of lace and diamond-studded combs. Looking closely, I could see that these beautiful women were all chewing tobacco! (62)

Close behind the Japanese, came the British secret agents. Even though England disliked the idea of the American cruise, they were determined to keep track of it and report their findings back home.

"The Stars and Stripes Forever."

I am told that only some of the money in this town comes from sheep herding. Most of it seems to come from smuggling. Rumor is there are more Havana cigars imported into Punta Arenas than into all the rest of Chile, so they must export them somewhere else. This small town couldn't possibly use all the millions of goods they import. (63) Interesting, don't you think?

I couldn't believe the bales of furs I saw all over town. I wasn't about to ask questions because this place was once a penal colony. Despite this, the men and officers still purchased several furs for their ladies back home at prices inflated for Punta Arenas standards, but not expensive by New York standards.

I also encountered hundreds of roaming children in the streets, doing nothing but looking us over. There was a constant swarm of fleas *everywhere*. We left Chile with red welts all over our faces and hands. (Minnie, I'm sorry; I searched and searched, but I just couldn't find the right fur that would be suitable for you. Ha, ha, ha.)

The process of coaling is different at each port. In Trinidad, we had six colliers and a six-day period in which to refuel. In Rio, there were five colliers and a nine-day period. Punta Arenas had only four colliers carrying 20,000 tons of coal, so only four battleships could be refueled at one time. To speed up the process so we could keep on schedule, we worked around the clock to finish the job.

Last night, with fresh coal in our hold, we set sail at 11:00 pm to reach Cape Forward before dawn. (64) We needed maximum daylight to be able to navigate the treacherous 140-mile stretch to Cape Pilar where the Magellan Strait meets the Pacific Ocean. (65) Veteran sailors of these waters tell us the next few days will be filled with long hours and a great deal of tension.

As I finish this letter, the fog is settling around us like a blanket. We can barely see the ship in front of us so we'll be using some different techniques for communication. With this, I must close. I don't believe with the work schedule set before me I will have time to write another letter until we down anchor.

I hope your holidays went well. I want to wish you a Happy Valentine's Day, Minnie, from your old-school chum.

Your friend,

Maurice

29 February 1908

Dear Frank and Minnie,

Our trip to Peru proved to be stressful as promised. It is a welcome reprieve to have this short break to write to you. I'm not sure when you will receive this letter, but I wanted to tell you about the last few days while they are fresh in my mind.

I closed my last letter right before we entered the Straits of Magellan. To navigate the first section of the strait, the ships formed a single column 400 yards apart. The column, led by the Chilean cruiser, *Chacabuco*, had three destroyers on either side. There was no possibility of stopping or dropping anchor for emergencies. For five days, we encountered thick fog. (66) We devised three different methods to communicate with the rest of the fleet: a steam whistle, searchlights, and a chip log. Each vessel used an aft light, to see the distance between the next ship in line more easily, and towed a chip log astern. A chip log is a spar with an upright board fastened to it at a predetermined distance, which throws up a spray that can be seen by the next ship in line to estimate the distance. (67) Each ship had to maintain ten knots to know precisely where she was in relationship to the others. Pretty clever, don't you think?

A new order was handed down during our run in the straits, which caused us to make a small detour in our original plans. When we were off the coast of Valparaiso, the entire fleet turned hard to starboard swinging the vessels around to the harbor so everyone on shore would be able to see us. We then picked up speed as we approached the coast, kicking up water for display. This maneuver is spectacular to watch. I hope you and Minnie get to see this display in California.

People from all over Chile— including many brass bands — lined the horseshoe bay. Two miles out, we saw on the green grassy hills beneath one of the terraces the word "Welcome" spelled out in enormous white letters. We had no idea how they had constructed such huge letters until part of the 'W' began to walk away! (68) The word was composed of hundreds of Chilean sailors, all in their whites, lying stationary and waiting one full hour for us to arrive. Using binoculars, we saw it took three men to create the height of just one letter! Our ships then discharged 1,200 rounds of ammunition, the likes of which I am sure have never before been heard in Chile. The noise was so deafening, frightened people raced back to the city in droves. Our bands played and we flew the signal flags.

The *New York Evening Mail* reported on February 20, 1908, that Admiral Evans was bed ridden. The gout had gotten the best of him and Rear Admiral Thomas had taken over the charge of the Fleet. The story was denied to protect the end of Evan's naval career.

When we were about 250 miles off the coast of Peru, on 20 February, two Peruvian cruisers joined us as escorts to Callao. I have to tell you we all were very exhausted. I was hoping no one would show up to greet us so that I could get some badly needed rest. It was very evident that our exhaustion was beginning to show when we steamed into the harbor, and the *Ohio's* anchor splashed into the water several seconds behind the rest of us.

As the battleships steamed through the Straits, Chile wired saying it was a direct insult that the fleet had stopped in Punta Arenas instead of Santiago. Evans decided to ease the tensions by displaying a pageant for Chile at sea.

Chile sent a goodwill message by wireless. The fleet turned, picked up speed and resumed its course to Peru.

Admiral Sperry wrote to the Department of the Navy complaining about the *Maine*, "Why her performances are tolerated is the one mystery of the fleet." (69)

The *Maine* was in pretty bad shape when she sailed into Peru. She was dirty, nearly out of coal, and she ruined the alignment by anchoring ten yards off her selected position! The *Alabama* with her cracked cylinders wasn't much better. She arrived with her hull streaked with black and yellow stains.

Callao's harbor was so crowded with small welcoming boats, we had to drop anchor two miles out. We were grateful that among the many vessels in port were five colliers, ready with our next supply of coal. We soon learned about several false rumors circulating weeks before our arrival that our fleet was ridden with the plague or that we were here to blow up the harbor. Another labeled all the men on board as thugs, murderers, and rapists. (70) I'm guessing it's a foreign plot to ruin our influence around the world.

CALLAO (Perú)

Peru was bickering with her South American neighbors. The visit of the American fleet gave her hope for the needed support from the United States. This anticipation spurred the Peruvians to empty their cash boxes creating lavish decorations and expensive parties. To plan the entertainment, two Peruvian spies were sent to Rio to view the festivities. Postal card shops were immediately supplied with plenty of cards and stamps for the fleet's visit. The Peruvians jailed a touring troupe of Japanese acrobats just to "please" and impress the Americans. (71)

The governor declared a holiday in Callao and Lima the day we arrived. All the stores and shops closed so everyone could enjoy the celebrations.

As soon as we were able to go ashore, we were welcomed with a plaster arch in the plaza and signs posted everywhere proclaiming America's greatness and power. We were met with Peruvians distributing pamphlets entitled *Here's happy days to the men of the American squadron!* Inside, the circular included facts on Callao and Lima, what to see and do as well as drink prices and even swear words in Spanish. (I'll save

CALLAO (Perú)
Desembarque de los Marineros Americanos 26 de Febrero 1908

4

that one for you, Frank!) Most of us elected to take the twenty-six-minute trolley ride to Lima. One window display in Lima caught my eye. It contained a large teddy bear, numerous bluejacket dolls, and sixteen miniature white battleships in celebration of our arrival. (72) I purchased postals here, and a small gift I think you will like, Minnie.

Besides attending the usual operas, banquets, receptions, and parties, the officers also had to attend services in the Incan Temple of the Sun, pay their respects to Pizarro's mummy, and accept the offer of a ride on the 'World's Highest Railway,' some 13,000 feet above sea level! Many officers had difficulty after living at sea level for so long. I heard Lieutenant Nicholas Seen, M.D., died from lack of oxygen while riding the railway. (73) Some officers suffered from the mountain sickness for several days after that ride. (Sometimes it pays not to be an officer!)

Minnie, you should see the hats the ladies balance on their heads. I hope you don't greet me wearing one of those, for I am sure you'd be courting a huge headache and I won't be able to see your face. They load their hats with all kinds of vegetables and fruits, the likes of which I have never seen before. I hope the trend doesn't spill onto American shores.

The main event in Lima staged for the fleet was a bullfight held on 24 February. We understood later Admiral Emory tried to avoid attending, afraid it would make him ill. I certainly wish I hadn't been so eager to go. President Pardo arranged special trains to hold 3,000 men

5000 AMERICAN SAILORS AT A BULL FIGHT IN LIMA PERU, FEB. 24, 1909.

and about 600 officers to take us to Lima for the event. Peruvian bands played while we marched from the station to the ring. We filled two-thirds of the arena while the officers and Lima's high society filled the boxes. I have to tell you, Frank, there were some beautiful Spanish ladies in those boxes! This fight, as my handbill stated, was to be the "grand gala" to honor our fleet.

The matadors killed six bulls that afternoon. The first four bulls were killed in honor of the admirals, the fifth bull in honor of the officers, and the sixth bull to honor all the enlisted men. Each bull wore a United States flag and a Peruvian banner around its neck. One bullfighter was killed and three others wounded. It took five or six matadors hacking away at the animal to finally subdue the beast. (74)

Many of our men became ill and left after the third bull was dragged out of the arena. Others stayed and cheered for the animals. I probably should have left too, but decided to stay with the rest of my buddies.

A bull named Shoe-fly, who'd been chosen for Admiral Sperry, grazed the matador in the chest. As they led the matador away, a picador stuck the bull with two quills that unfurled the American flag.

That was enough for one of my buddies. He jumped from the stands and into the arena running toward Old Glory. He wasn't about to let the emblem of our country be trampled upon! (75) What a gift they bestowed upon us all in honor of the fleet; one man killed by a bull, another seriously injured, and a badly gored horse. (76)

We departed Callao this morning at 10:00 am, but not before an interesting mishap occurred. As we performed our maneuvers, the *Ohio* signaled a sailor went overboard, and she could not get out of formation to pick him up. Just as the *Georgia* lowered a small launch to rescue the sailor, a motorboat sped by and picked him up from the water. We found out later the Bluejacket was a deserter who'd *paid* to have the motorboat rescue him!

We are now safely on our way, and approaching the coast of California. As you know, once we are out to sea there's little time for letter writing. Hopefully, I'll have some time before target practice in Magdalena Bay for another letter. Looking forward to our visit in Los Angeles.

My best to both of you.

Your friend,

Maurice

Two days before the *Connecticut* gave the farewell gala, the entertainment fund was depleted. The candy was gone and so were the 15,000 pounds of bonbons. Evans cabled Washington and requested another $2,000. Unfortunately, the money did not arrive in time for their party. A few wilted ferns and some potted plants on top of the turrets were all the decorations that could be organized by Henry Reuterdahl.

At this point in the cruise, word was out that Reuterdahl was the correspondent for *McClure's* magazine. Reuterdahl knew it would be only a short while before he would be sent ashore. Some sources say President Roosevelt ordered him ashore before the fleet's departure from Callao; other sources say he left due to a family emergency. But leave he did and he was able to obtain a berth on the *Culgoa* going to San Diego.

People who read about the generous party given aboard the *Minnesota* in Rio were very disappointed with the *Connecticut's* attempted effort in Callao. The Peruvians were also irritated with the short nine-day visit after the fleet had spent ten days in Rio. Ecuador was upset that her invitation was turned down, and the fleet would sail right past her. Colombia never sent an invitation to the fleet as they were still harboring a dislike for the Americans since the takeover of Panama in 1903.

MAGDALENA BAY

1814 – PASO ROBLES HOT SPRINGS, CALIFORNIA. WHERE ADMIRAL EVANS RECUPERATED ON THE
VISIT OF THE ATLANTIC FLEET TO THE PACIFIC.
ON THE ROAD OF A THOUSAND WONDERS. SOUTHERN PACIFIC.

While anchored in Magdalena Bay, an unmanned sentry post was discovered on the *Kearsarge*. The next morning a full stick of dynamite was found in the coal being delivered to the *Kentucky*, so all watches were doubled.

12 April 1908

Dear Minnie and Frank,

The last month has been busy, with only enough time for short notes on the backs of postcards. I have a couple of hours now so will try to bring you up to date.

We dropped anchor in Magdalena Bay, Mexico at daybreak on 12 March with no greetings or receptions from shore. Surrounding the bay is a desert-like area with a small tent city of bars and gambling houses. This stop was scheduled to take on more coal, have target practice, (which we have to do at least twice a year), drill for the parades that we expect in California, and to give our ships another fresh coat of paint. In between these duties, we were free to hunt, fish, and look for any Japanese spies hanging around.

By the time you get this letter, you will probably have read in the newspaper that on 14 March, Admiral Evans announced he would be stepping down from his duties when the fleet reaches San Francisco due

A Navy Target before being fired at.
© N. Moser, N. Y.

The result of one round of practice firing at Magdalena Bay, Mexico, March, 1908. Each head represents a hole in the target.

2571

to his health. No one was surprised. The *USS Yankton* carried him from Magdalena Bay to the hot springs near Paso Robles, California. He'll rest in Paso Robles for two months so he'll be able to take part in the celebrations in Frisco.

Rear-Admiral Thomas transferred his flag from the *Minnesota* to the *Connecticut* to take command in Evans' absence, and Rear-Admiral Sperry became the second in command. Captain Schroeder, the captain of our ship, now commands the Fourth Division, and Captain Alexander Sharp is the commander of our ship, the *Virginia*.

Let me explain a little about target practice, Frank. As I said before, the Navy calls for target practice twice a year: once for what is called *record* and once for battle practice. Record practice is held to qualify the gun pointers or the best shooters. Battle practice provides shooters an opportunity to show how skilled they have become. (77) I can't tell you how much I dislike this time every year. We had target practice from 12 March to 3 April— including Sundays— drilling all day and half the night. The din on board became deafening! Every time we have target practice, I get so nervous I can hardly sleep afterward. You know I've done my fair share of shooting rabbits and coons, but the tension during this time aboard ship is awful.

Like the guns themselves, target practice takes a well-oiled team. Twenty men are assigned specific posts that include: section chief, gunner, range-keeper, breech detail, rammer detail, elevating detail, ammunition bearers and others. Practice begins when one of the ships steams in front of the previously placed targets. (Enclosed are some postals for better understanding.) The ships' steam whistle signals for simultaneous firing to commence.

The section chief, standing two yards in the rear of the breech, gives the command "Posts!" and twenty trained men move to their positions. Two men are responsible in sighting the great rifles: one to control the horizontal range, and the other to train the gun vertically lining up the shot. Three men are required at the breech (the back end of the gun), while three others control the electrical rammers that press the ammunition into the firing mechanism. Several men are constantly at work in the handling room loading the ammunition hoists with projectiles and powder charges. (78) It's not unusual for a crew to take twelve shots in a little over five minutes.

During that short time, projectiles of six tons are fired through a single gun by the explosion of two tons of powder which have been brought up from the magazines and handling room some forty-five feet below the gun with a hoist. The hoist immediately descends for another load and is on its way to the gun before the previous charge is fired. (79) Once the gun is fired; the breech is opened, and a man with padded gloves removes the empty powder case, which has been heated to a red-hot temperature. (80) Then, the dance starts again.

After a string of shots, the torn pieces of canvas around the holes in the targets are painted red to distinguish them from the hits made during the following run.

A group of men hauls the targets out to their position by tugboat, and that's where the crew remains all day repairing the marks and the rafts that hold the targets. Even the noon meal is brought out to these men. When the last shot is fired, the crew sets up the targets for the following day and then returns to the ship.

There was only one mishap during our target practice in Magdalena Bay. The *Missouri,* or the "Misery" as we now call her, had a six-inch cannon blow out during her practice. They had to replaced it with a painted wooden one. Can you imagine the ribbing the men are getting over there? They are the only ship in the entire Navy with a wooden gun!

On 11 April, no one was more thrilled than I to hear the familiar cry "up anchor" for it meant we could now head for God's country: the United States of America! It will be just a short while until our visit. Have a safe trip to your aunt's place in Santa Ana.

Your friend,

Maurice

The weeks after the visit to Peru, President Roosevelt received invitations from Australia, New Zealand, Japan, and China requesting a visit from the Atlantic fleet. Australia was nervous about the problems brewing with the Japanese. She was upset that the British Royal Navy appeared more concerned about Germany than Japan, and had withdrawn from the Pacific leaving New Zealand and Australia unprotected. From their viewpoint, the promise of a visit from the American fleet could only mean the United States was coming to their rescue. England finally approved the visit, and the two countries began preparing for the big event as a demonstration against Japan. (81)

In February 1908, the United States signed an agreement with Japan concerning the immigration problem in California. A month later, on March 18, Japan sent an invitation to the American fleet. "The Imperial Government are firmly convinced of the reassuring effect which the visit of American Fleet to the shores of Japan will produce upon the traditional relations of good understanding and mutual sympathy which so happily exist between the two nations." (82) Roosevelt was astounded when he received the invite. He felt this would be a great way to handle Japan, convinced the only risk involved was the alliance with England. Germany's Kaiser Wilhelm, displeased about the fleet's proposed visit to Japan, began writing friendlier letters to Roosevelt while simultaneously spreading more rumors about possible Japanese invasions.

China felt the United States should support them because of the Open Door Policy, which, in 1900, had declared America's intent to "preserve Chinese territorial and administrative entity," as well as the Anglo-Treaty. (83) After much negotiation, Roosevelt accepted an invitation from China on March 25. The main problem was to locate an adequate harbor for the fleet to drop anchor. It proved to be a challenge for the fleet to give Japan and China, who were the bitterest of enemies, equal time and to not show favoritism.

By the middle of March, the fleet had traveled 14,000 miles with minimal mechanical breakdowns, showing its superiority over the Russian fleet of 1905. In fact, Evans stated the fleet was in better condition than when it departed Hampton Roads in December. Japan and England joined the other nations with praises of the success of the fleet in its first part of the journey. Fears concerning our unprotected coastlines proved to be unfounded as Americans felt more secure knowing a fleet of battleships could reach the coast of California ready for battle.

Since the beginning of the cruise, there had been seven deaths and 152 hospitalizations. Cases of smallpox, meningitis, typhoid, and pneumonia were reported.

A Glorious Christmas

Back home, Americans bought models of the *Connecticut* and teddy bears sold in toy stores. Boater hats became the rage for women, and sailor suits were sold for children. Maps were purchased and posted on the walls of homes and schools to trace the route of the fleet. Ads in magazines carried the pictures of the fleet on containers of pipe tobacco, Studebaker cars, and pianolas —a form of player piano. Prudential Life Insurance superimposed the battleships on its Gibraltar picture for their advertisements. Songs and poems were written and published to celebrate the visit of the fleet in many American ports.

The Democratic Congress had long ago opposed the idea of a cruise to the Pacific, but When President Roosevelt presented the multitude of invitations and acceptance letters, there was nothing the congressmen could do. The Democrats felt it was wrong for the President to dictate the comings and goings of a naval fleet. Congress felt it was also wrong for the Navy to exhibit itself all over the world at the expense of the taxpayers. The now Republican Congress, however, voted to add two new battleships to the fleet with construction to begin in April 1908.

SAN DIEGO, CALIFORNIA

The Pacific West Coast spent months preparing for the arrival of their American fleet. The restaurateurs, amusement specialists, gamblers, skin-game artists, as well as other legitimate and semi-legitimate operators, who made it their business to prey on the easily available sailors, also made preparations. "These people first set up their wares in San Diego and traveled from town to town as the fleet progressed slowly northward. Almost every vacant lot . . . was rented by these gentry, and hastily constructed, cheap booths, colorful with red, white and blue bunting, were set up." (84) Postcards were designed and printed to be sold to the servicemen and tourists as a way to remember this small slice of history.

H. H. Stratton, from Chattanooga, Tennessee, was the only postcard publisher who had been granted permission to travel with the fleet. Due to the extended stay scheduled in San Francisco, however, other card publishers knew there would be time for their souvenirs to be purchased. The Pacific Novelty Company, W. Kimball Briggs Company, and Britton & Rey Lithographers produced collectible cards. Other publishers from Los Angeles, Ocean Park, Oakland, and Seattle also saw the opportunity to create memorable cards commemorating the visit of the fleet.

The popular *Sunset Magazine* had published an article the previous October stating that the Pacific Coast did not have the docks or the facilities available to paint and clean the ships, nor was it prepared to take care of a fleet of this size. The article, however, did not deter the coastal cities of California from battling for the privilege of entertaining the fleet. Each presented its own plea and invitation to President Roosevelt. The only way the Navy could satisfy the coastal cities was to break the fleet into several groups. San Diego, San Pedro, Redondo Beach and Santa Cruz considered the split an insult and would not tolerate it. Their invitations to President Roosevelt were for all the ships or none at all to visit their ports. In addition, each city demanded the fleet arrive on a specified date and time.

San Pedro threatened to refund the $10,000 in entertainment contributions when she heard the fleet was going to stay longer in Redondo Beach than in her harbor. The bickering continued up the coast.

15 April 1908

Dear Minnie and Frank,

Until now, my busy schedule has made it difficult to find time to write a decent letter. I also promised my mother I would write to her as often as possible. I am hopeful this letter and the postals will be received before our visit to Los Angles

When we sailed past the United States border, the celebrations surpassed all others. There was a lot of excitement on board as we watched the throngs of welcoming crowds on shore cheering and waving their hats as we steamed past. Indeed, what a wonderful sight it was! At 1:00 pm, yesterday, we dropped anchor off the Hotel Del Coronado and began the celebrations. We couldn't anchor in San Diego's harbor

THE FLEET IN CALIFORNIA WATERS. COPYRIGHT 1908 BY N.R. JACKSON. NO. 0097.

Landing at San Diego, Calif., April 11, 1908.
First landing on American soil since leaving Hampton Roads,
December 16, 1907.

because it is too shallow for our huge battleships. I heard the people there were disappointed because we were not willing to risk our ships in their shallow harbor. They just can't be thinking straight!

The next day, all was forgiven because local boats rowed out to where we were anchored bearing thousands of oranges. Another boat visited each ship, carrying young women with armfuls of flowers. (85) Not one of those women was as lovely or as beautiful as you, Minnie.

San Diego's festivities began with a parade, the first of many for California. Small boats ferried us the ten miles from our ships to the foot of the parade route. Bluejackets from sixty-four companies and Marines from sixteen companies numbering 5,000 men marched for three miles to receive the State of California's official welcome at the grandstand. Governor Gillett gave the welcoming speech, and Rear Admiral Thomas announced that "the celebration without Admiral Evans, was like a play of Hamlet without Hamlet in the picture." (86)

The day was a grueling ten hours. You know I am not fond of marching and performing in parades. Not only was it hot, dusty, and tiresome, but the spectators also had problems. (87) I guess they underestimated the vast number of people who would attend the festivities. Hundreds of people were seen running around wildly through the streets trying to find a place to stay the night. (88)

It was easy to see that a lot of money had been put into the decorations around the city and hardly any money into the parade itself, there was only one float! As we marched, I noticed thousands of school children off in the distance clustered together waving flags. Because of the disorganization of the crowds, these children were so overpowered they couldn't see much of our parade. I felt a little sorry for them.

You know, I was just as excited as everyone else when we arrived in California, but after that exhausting parade, I was thankful I didn't have liberty. Only 75 men from each ship were granted leave for the first two days of our visit. I simply returned to the ship and rested; I want to be in good shape for our meeting. Because of the huge crowds of people, San Diego couldn't accommodate very many men on shore leave anyway.

Once again, I was thankful not to have the rank of officer. They had to attend a grand ball held in the Coronado Hotel after the parade. San Diego must have thought it successful because the next day the newspapers reported the ball had been the "most brilliant function in the city's history'." (89)

17 April

Tonight is the last night of our visit in San Diego with yet another ball for the officers at the Hotel Del Coronado. I understand you have cousins who spent their honeymoon there a few years back. What a beautiful hotel. I hope, Minnie, the two of us can visit it together someday.

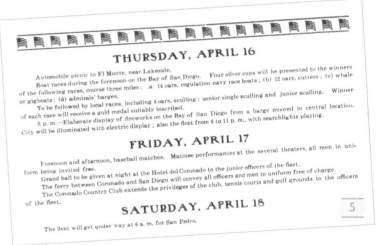

I am anxiously awaiting the morning hours when we set sail. I'm so looking forward to seeing you again my friends, and having you show me Los Angeles, your "City of Angels." I know you'll be waving on the shore along with your Aunt Em as we steam up the coast. Know that I will be waving as well when we sail past Newport Harbor.

With much anticipation,

Maurice

To eliminate the problems experienced in San Diego with the uncontrolled large crowds, the principal of the Santa Barbara High School viewed their parade in hopes of improving the situation when the fleet reached his city. He wanted to make sure that when the fleet left Santa Barbara, the world would realize Santa Barbara knew how to treat the powerful American Navy.

On Wednesday, April 22, 1908, The *Santa Barbara Morning Press* reported the men mailed over 1,000,000 postcards while visiting San Diego, most of the cards going to the southern states. "Postmaster D. F. Hunt and his clerks are expecting the most tremendous rush ever experienced by the local post office when the fleet arrives at this city. It is believed that the Christmas holiday season records will be retired to the realm of insignificance by the demands made upon the office by the public during the stay of the fleet here. If the experience of San Diego is any criterion, the Santa Barbara post office is to have a most strenuous five days." The "office (San Diego post office), had dispatched ten pouches of first-class mail daily; fifty sacks of third and fourth class matter; looked after two trips daily from mail orderlies from each of the sixteen ships; employed two clerks to do nothing else save 'facing up' mail, that is turning all matter so that they lay face upward, for stamping . . ." (90)

Off New Port; 18th April 08

SAN PEDRO, CALIFORNIA

U. S. Battleships entering San Pedro Harbor, California.

The fleet left San Diego Saturday, 18 April at 6:00 am for San Pedro, the harbor of Los Angeles. Even at that early hour, spectators lined the shore to see the battleships steam away in formation. People continued to arrive along the beaches north of San Diego during the day to watch the ships steam past in single file. Frank, Minnie and Aunt Em drove Aunt Em's rig from Santa Anna to Newport Beach to join the throng of sightseers eager to witness the historic event. Frank, as always, carried his camera and took pictures to make into postcards as souvenirs.

The fleet reached San Pedro harbor at 2:55 pm to find 100,000 people on shore, many more people than had greeted them in San Diego. All sixteen ships dropped anchor for an overnight stay while thousands of visitors swarmed over them. Many of these overly zealous people had to be fished out of the water. The *Connecticut, Vermont, Louisiana,* and the *Kansas* anchored inside the harbor, while the other three divisions anchored outside. The streets were lined

with souvenir and postcard peddlers, waving flags to induce the sailor to spend his pay. As soon as the men came ashore, they were kissed and hugged by girls wearing red, white, and blue striped dresses created especially for the occasion. Wives and girlfriends who had traveled from the East Coast joined the throng to look for their sweethearts. (91) Among the joyous crowds were Minnie and Frank searching for a glimpse of Maurice on the *Virginia*. What a thrilling day it must have been for all of them. One can only speculate about what transpired during the stay in San Pedro. From that day forward, letters and/or postcards were written daily between Maurice and Minnie; Maurice had finally succeeded in getting Minnie's attention.

The first evening in San Pedro, the fleet put on a spectacular light show. The warships flashed their lights upward and crisscrossed them toward the harbor forming fantastic designs while the vessels remained individually lit. There were so many people gathered to watch the show that many had trouble finding transportation back home and had to stayed ashore for the night.

The following morning, the fleet separated and divided into four divisions to spend the next five days at the various ports of Long Beach, Santa Monica and Redondo. The first group remained anchored in San Pedro.

Los Angles did not require a parade from the fleet. Nevertheless, the Marines and Bluejackets marched for the spectators every day before lunch. Over the next few days, hot air balloon ascensions, prizefights, fencing matches, rodeos, and barbecues were staged to occupy the Bluejackets' time from early morning until late evening. Maurice had no trouble staying occupied with Frank and Minnie showing him around town.

The newspaper reporters, known for their realism, couldn't figure out what all the fuss was about. They felt the sailors had done nothing to warrant such celebrity but eat, dance, party, parade and attend to the women in South American countries.

On Thursday, 23 April, automobile tours to Los Angeles were scheduled for 250 officers. The officers and men received the welcome gift of two California oranges a piece. Oranges were not readily available in other parts of the country and represented a special treat. After the automobile tour, the officers enjoyed a mid-day luncheon in Pasadena, then visited Hollywood and Santa Monica. The following day the same event was repeated for the 3,000 enlisted men who had accepted the invitation. Frank

American Battle Ship Fleet Sailors.

Barbecue held at Chutes Park Los Angeles Cal

captured a picture of Maurice and his buddies to create a postcard as they began their tour in an automobile decked out with American flags. Maurice wrote on the back of this card, sending it to Minnie from San Francisco, "I am sending the postcard that Frank had printed of our automobile tour in L. A. I do wish you and I had been in this car together, oh who would drive? I guess we would just let her rip wouldn't we!"

A huge feast was prepared for the men after their auto tour. The sailors consumed 5,000 pounds of barbecued beef, 300 pounds of fresh butter, (92) 5,000 hot rolls, 500 pounds of Spanish beans with chili con carne, and 500 gallons of coffee. Approximately 1,500 yards of cloth were used to cover all the tables. (93) Freshly picked roses adorned the center of each table. Part of the entertainment during the luncheon was a Wild West show, which must have resembled the show given by Wild Bill Cody himself years ago. After the tour, many men were taken as guests to residents' homes for meals and relaxation. Spending his leave time visiting the tourist areas with Frank and

The Sailors' Barbecue at Los Angeles, California, during Fleet Week, April 18th to 28th. Los Angeles For Me.

Minnie, he quickly decided Los Angeles was his favorite place, a place he would want to live. He knew he would return to the area someday, and he hoped Minnie would accompany him.

A banquet at the Hotel Alexandria in Los Angeles was given for the Admirals and the dignitaries of the city and state. The hotel had been closed to guests for four days, keeping the decorations and the menu a secret. Beautiful flowers — abundant in Southern California — filled the hotel. Robert D. Jones felt the celebrations Los Angles had prepared for the fleet's visit were totally for the enjoyment of the men they now considered heroes and not to see how much money they could make or the advantages they might gain. The men all noticed the sincerity of Los Angeles after experiencing so many grafters in other ports.

Minnie and Frank left the area: Minnie to return home, and Frank to travel by train to San Francisco to explore the area with Maurice.

Saturday, 25 April, at 5:00 pm, the fleet divisions left their various ports to conduct maneuvers off Venice, Ocean Park, and Santa Monica.

They reassembled at Santa Monica before continuing North to Santa Barbara. At each of these ports, people slept overnight on the beaches waiting for the fleet's arrival. On 26 April, the *Santa Barbara Morning Press* reported thousands of people had been sleeping on the shores, and thousands of others had passed the night in the streets, all unable to secure sleeping accommodations. People brought tents and blankets. Some residents even allowed visitors to sleep on their lawns. Others climbed rooftops only to have the fog roll in, partially obstructing their view. In Santa Monica, the unbroken line of people stretched for five miles along the beach.

The merchants of Santa Barbara had a hay day the week before the arrival of the fleet. An ad in the local newspaper stated, "The sight of a lifetime, once seen will never be forgotten. Let us show our appreciation, and do ourselves proud in the welcome we extend to the preservers of our country. Santa Barbara will do her part royally and well; for this, we are assured. Everybody will look their best. The best suit, the most attractive dress, the prettiest waist, the handsomest hat, the swellest pair of shoes will be brought out and worn; and if what is at hand is not good enough, new will be bought to take its place. Here is where we will come in: Here is where we will shine. Here is where we will add our quota to the general helpfulness of the celebration. We will make it possible for every lady in Santa Barbara to have a handsome garment at a saving price such as she can afford to pay..." (94) Similar ads appeared in newspapers up and down the Pacific coast.

SANTA BARBARA, CALIFORNIA

Battleships at Santa Barbara, Cal.

2 May 1908

Dear Minnie,

How difficult it was to up anchor after such a short visit with you. However, I'm reassured that it will not be our last. I'll send you more postcards when we arrive in Frisco, as we will be staying there longer affording me more time. Do you have an album in which to keep these cards? I'll be on the lookout for one if you wish.

After we left San Pedro, we sailed the short distance to Santa Barbara arriving at 4:00 pm 25 April. Civilian boats circled our ships, and we exchanged cheers. I understand these people have kept daily track of our cruise for months. They were puzzled and thrilled that the *Big Sixteen* would visit their small city which has a small population of between 8 to 9,000. People paid four bits to have the privilege of going out on the wharf and securing passage on one of the small boats to sail out to see our fleet!

Much as we all hate war, and all that goes with it, our white warships flying the Stars and Stripes steaming toward the shore must have been a powerful sight to the many people sitting on a hillside above the bay in the bright April sunshine. (95)

Almost every empty building was used for temporary restaurants, and nearly every vacant lot was used for vendors. Minnie, let me tell you about one of the vendors. (I didn't see him in Los Angeles; if he was there, I'm grateful we missed him!) There was always a crowd at this booth, so I decided to check it out for myself. This vendor had set up a counter holding several cheap baseballs. About thirty feet behind the counter stood a Negro in front of a drape with his head poking through a horse collar. Two bits got you three baseballs to throw at the Negro's head. The poor man dodged the balls as best as possible but more

"Two bits" is 25 cents or one quarter]

times than not, the sailor's throw reached the intended target. (96) My goodness, wasn't your grandfather an abolitionist? Wouldn't he roll over in his grave to have seen such goings on?

Tell Frank the nickel beer we had in Los Angeles went up to 50 cents here, and the 50 cent meals jumped to $3.00!

The Potter Hotel from the Boulevard, Santa Barbara, Cal.

The officers' wives who followed the fleet up the coast also complained about the high cost of their hotel rooms in the Potter Hotel. Most of us didn't bother with Santa Barbara. We felt more comfortable either staying aboard ship or taking the train to Los Angeles where the prices were better. I'm just sorry you had already left for Santa Ana!

Parting from you was difficult, yet the joy to discover you, my dearest Minnie, have a soft spot in your heart for me, will help me survive the grueling activities during the remainder of the cruise.

I am sure you will read about this predicament in the papers, so let me clear up the situation for you. Because of the high prices imposed on us, two sailors — with the help of their fellow Bluejackets — demolished a restaurant in Santa Barbara. I won't say whether I knew these fellows or not, but they entered one of the five-day restaurants that were set up just for our benefit and ordered a steak dinner. At the end of the meal, these men were presented with a bill of $7.00! In Los Angeles, wasn't the price we paid for that good T-bone steak around one dollar?

Sailors Parade at the Flower Festival, Santa Barbara, Calif., April 28, 1908.

Anyway, they refused to pay the tab. An argument followed, and the police were summoned. The Santa Barbara police agreed with the sailors, but because they didn't ask for the price of the steak dinner before ordering, they were forced to pay the bill. Later that night, a large group of sailors returned to the restaurant. They grabbed table legs, chairs, and anything else they could use to wreck the entire establishment. (97) Public opinion was on the side of the sailors, though, so not a single citation was issued. The locals said that the mayor had called the saloonkeepers and the restaurant owners into a conference at city hall more than a week before our arrival. The proprietors all agreed they would not inflate their prices when the sailors arrived, (98) and they wouldn't sell liquor to any man who had already had enough.

Visiting hours to board and visit our ships were set for Sunday. Santa Barbara was no different than the other ports where we have anchored. When citizens visit our ship, they always walk away with spoons, cups, bowls, and whatever else they can conceal on their person!

Monday was the parade, and what a parade it was. The town nicknamed it the *Parade of Flowers*, and for a good reason. The floral show became a flower battle, and everybody got into the act. A few days before we arrived, the newspaper asked all the residents to bring their flowers, no matter how few, into the city. The organizers of the show put Steward Edward White, the famous author, in charge of the parade. "Strip your garden for the occasion. The blossoms can never be put to a better use." Mr. White organized high school students into small groups to prepare bouquets of flowers small enough to fit into a gun barrel. Each group was then assigned a certain squadron and was told the time to meet them on the wharf. The boys carried the bouquets to the wharf in tubs of water to keep them fresh. When we came on shore, a group of women greeted us and put a bouquet in each gun barrel as we marched in formation from the wharf onto State Street. (99)

Between the admiral's box and the press box on the parade route, officials had veterans of the Civil War sit on benches each holding a little girl on his knee who was dressed in white and wore a red wreath on her head. To make peace with the city, Admiral Thomas reluctantly agreed to be carried on one of the flower floats drawn by six horses during the parade. (100) Seven horseless carriages, I understand those were all Santa Barbara had, sputtered their way along the parade route. (101) We reached the city's plaza after marching with bouquets of flowers in the muzzles of our rifles. That's when the battle of the flowers took place. We were bombarded with tons of blossoms. Admiral Thomas set the example for us by catching the bouquets while still in mid-air and tossing them back at the riders and drivers. Well, you can imagine what followed! We have never been so attacked.

After the parade had settled down, there was a reception, a dinner, a ball, as well as the dance of the flowers. These celebrations, however, were only presented for the officers and townspeople in a tent placed at the Plaza del Mar. The tent was lit with electrical lights, which I hadn't seen much during this cruise. I understand the celebration put quite a strain on the Edison Company, so the Potter Hotel had to give up some of their electrical supply for the event. An informal dance was given for the men on a canvas covered boat yard, but after *that* crazy parade, I just wanted to get back to my ship. Besides, there was only one lady I wanted to dance with, and she wasn't here.

Sporting events and horseback riding had been arranged for all the Bluejackets on Tuesday and Wednesday. I hadn't ridden a horse in four years, and after a full day's ride, I didn't think I'd be able to pull duty that night. I was sure my legs would never operate in quite the same way again! I'm fine now. The only other activity I took in was a tour of the mission led by one of the priests. Have you been there? I found the tour very entertaining.

After the likes of Los Angles, my buddies and me have decided that Santa Barbara is not a good port for liberty. Even the officers willingly admitted they had found the celebrations impossible, ridiculous, and hideous. They were tired of having to play this game on their own soil: always wearing a smile, never yawning, and always at the mercy of some committee. Regular shore patrols were instituted again. Hired livery wagons were sent to town to take sailors who had become disorderly back to their ships. I saw quite a few of these sailors returning. (102) To make matters worse, the *Kentucky* caught fire. I'm told it was caused by a spontaneous combustion in the coal bunker. Fortunately, it was quickly contained.

Thursday, 30 April, we upped our anchors. We steamed past Pismo Beach — much to the disappointment, I'm sure, of the crowds waving to us from shore — and on to Monterey Bay. A rumor is spreading that Pismo Beach officials have condemned Santa Barbara, saying they hogged the fleet to themselves.

On to Frisco, Minnie. I will find some pretty postals and perhaps a gift or two for the Little Girl while stationed there. Looking forward to spending more time with Frank.

Love,

Maurice

A stop was not originally scheduled for Monterey because her harbor was not adequate for that many battleships, but when Monterey learned of a planned pageant in Santa Cruz, she did not want to be left out of the celebrations. Admiral Thomas finally agreed to split the fleet to allow Monterey to stage a pageant similar to the one planned in Santa Cruz.

One mishap occurred while anchored in Monterey. "A gale swept the unprotected anchorage, breaking the *Illinois* off her chain and blowing her half a mile through the formation. Emergency anchors caught just as she was about to strike the *Alabama*. So narrow was the miss, that the latter's gangway was sheared off and Admiral Sperry's barge crushed between the hulls." (103)

When the fleet reassembled at Santa Cruz on 4 May, Henry Rueterdahl (hired by an eastern magazine he was commissioned to paint the ships as they came through the Golden Gate) rejoined the *Minnesota*. Commander Evans joined the fleet in Santa Cruz, arriving by train from Paso Robles. Evans claimed to be feeling better than ever but remained in his cabin giving the command to Admiral Ingersoll for the trip to San Francisco.

SAN FRANCISCO, CALIFORNIA

Two years of rebuilding after the earthquake of 1906, San Francisco still lay in ruins; the people were ready for a celebration. A local report said, "The arrival harmonizes with the second anniversary of the Great Fire, and the eyes of the world will naturally be turned to the 'Queen City of the Pacific' to see that stupendous work accomplished in repairing the devastation wrought by that great catastrophe." (104)

For months San Francisco and Oakland prepared for this event. Private parties donated all the money to entertain the officers, 8,000 Bluejackets and 500 Marines for the fleet's twelve-day visitation. The average donation was between $50 and $100, with many offerings as little as 50 cents. The American Steel and Wire Company gave the largest donation at $2,000.

CALIFORNIA OPENS WIDE HER GOLDEN GATE IN WELCOME TO THE FLEET.

Thursday, 7 May 1908

Dear Minnie,

Resuming our formation, we left Santa Cruz yesterday for the short sail northward. Just before we entered the San Francisco Bay, we were met by eight armored cruisers from the Pacific fleet. The fog was so thick it seemed to hug the water. But at precisely noon, the clouds lifted to reveal forty-two warships including eighteen battleships, six destroyers, and six auxiliaries. (105) We were joined by every gunboat and torpedo boat on the West Coast.

Today, the newspaper estimated over one million people crowded the waterfront, rooftops, and private boats, while thousands of spectators blackened the surrounding hills waving flags —more people than I had ever seen in my life. We could see many had brought tents and the paper further stated a few were able to rent view windows on Telegraph Hill to witness this event. I wish you could have been here. Goat Island looked as if a huge flock of small birds had settled upon it. (106) I also read that the railroads estimated they had brought about 300,000 people into the city during the forty-eight hours before our arrival. No wonder we saw so many tents!

A huge hot air balloon greeted us stringing two side-by-side large banners, saying Welcome Examiner— our greeting from the local newspaper, the *San Francisco Examiner*. Oil and gasoline fueled the

ALANTIC FLEET ENTERING THE GOLDEN GATE SANFRANCISCO.

Yerba Buena Island was called Goat Island.

The arrival of the fleet "inaugurated a romance between Market Street and Navy uniforms that lasted until civvies were certified for shore leave after World War II"(107)

Battleship Fleet, S.F. May, 1908.

Battle Ships at Night in San Francisco Bay, Cal.

balloon while it was controlled by an aeronaut from Australia. That aeronaut did not have an easy task. The balloon had to rise about 2,500 feet to be above our ships. When the balloon was right above us, the Aeronaut swung by his legs on a trapeze, leaving his hands free to hold American flags and wave to us. I'm including the picture that appeared in the paper so you can get a better idea of what I'm talking about.

Ferries, schooners, tugs, and yachts were all over the bay making as much racket as possible. The Presidio and Fort Baker shot their cannons, and we saluted back. This began the celebrations.

Last night, Frisco saw twenty-six battleships flying banners and flags with shimmering lights that illuminated each ship's name. I am sure this beautiful sight could be seen for miles. Each night we are in harbor we'll continue this practice. We all stayed aboard last night resting up for the parade scheduled for today. The officers weren't so lucky however; they had to attend a reception and ball held at the newly opened Fairmont Hotel.

Minnie, what a parade we had today! You thought the march in Los Angeles was spectacular, I wish you could have seen this one. There were approximately 7,500 Marines and Bluejackets accompanied by over 2,000 federal troops from the San Francisco area paraded down Market Street and what looked like a newly paved Van Ness Avenue.

I left the *Virginia* at 7:00 pm and didn't return until 2:00 am this morning! We were granted shore leave after the parade, so not only

8   The Great Naval Parade at San Francisco. May 8, 1908.

2509

did I buy these postals to share some of the sights of the city with you, but I was able to reunite with Frank. The beautiful buildings and new skyscrapers are amazing. Some are as high as three stories! I'll make sure Frank takes these back to you when he returns. You readily notice the Californianism in these pretty vistas, just like the tropics, except it's pretty windy here.

It is late, and I must now sleep. Secretary of the Navy, Victor H. Metcalf will be reviewing our fleet and the Pacific Fleet, while aboard the *Yorktown* in just a few hours. That means we'll be playing the National Anthem for quite a while tomorrow. Sweet dreams, my Little Girl.

Maurice

There were two hostile political groups who hosted the entertainment in San Francisco: the *bad millionaires*, who were following Mayor E. E Schmitz; and the *good millionaires*, those of the reformed group. The two groups never mixed socially, which meant that all events had to be duplicated. Evans had his wheelchair pulled by a rope behind his open carriage to take him to the various functions. (108) All along the way, roses were thrown in his path and the people shouted, "Fighting Bob, Fighting Bob!"

Fleet Parade, May, 1908

That evening a Hawaiian banquet was held in the St. Francis Hotel to honor the officers and the Secretary of the Navy after the review of the battleships. The ballroom was "stuffed with swaying bamboos, live canaries, and ukuleles." (109) There were numerous courses and many wines to feed the guests and many more speeches. Admiral Evans was wheeled into the banquet room to make his farewell speech attacking Henry Reuterdahl for his publicized criticism of the battleships. The citizens were so anxious for details, that the *San Francisco Chronicle* printed all 2,500 names of the guests who attended the ball. (110)

Saturday, 10 May

Dear Minnie,

So how is my Little Girl today? It's sure busy here in Frisco!

Yesterday, Rear Admiral Evans officially stepped down, and the command was temporarily given to Admiral Thomas. Now Thomas will have to attend all the parties and give all the speeches Admiral Evans was to give.

So far, boys show up every morning on the pier to sell their newspapers and postcards. It's a good way to get an idea about the city. The day after the parade, the *Examiner* published a couple of cartoons picturing men as they watched our parade. I thought you would get a smile out of this one because you know my dislike of women's hats. One cartoon showed a group of women all wearing the latest style hat, the wide-brimmed Merry Widow, admiring the sailors. The unlucky man behind the hats turned to one of the other men and said, "Curses!" For they had seen nothing of the parade because of those huge hats! Another cartoon I thought interesting was a Japanese man with his hands in his pockets walking away from the city with a thought bubble that said: "I must think this thing over!" The caption read: "He came, he saw, he went home in a meditative mood." (111) As I am sure you have read, relations with Japan are not very good right now. The *Chronicle* also reported on our parade, "They are a clean, fresh-looking lot of young men of manly appearances and bearing. If any of our people should attempt to swindle or overcharge them, the wrath of the community would be visited on them."(112) Don't you agree? We are a pretty decent lot!

Marines of the Pacific Fleet S.F. May 7, 1908

Yesterday was Oakland Day as well as a children's day to visit our ships. No child under the age of six was allowed on board, thank goodness, and those under nine needed a guardian to accompany them. Frisco is proving to be no different than any other port we have visited. There are always those people who feel they can walk anywhere on the ship and take anything in sight. Some have even walked right into an officer's private room or simply stolen a piece of silverware for a souvenir.

Oakland is just across the bay from Frisco, and yes, we marched in yet another parade. The people here were even more enthusiastic than in San Francisco! We began the march on Broadway to 20th Street, then we headed east to Boulevard, and on to Adams Point where we gorged ourselves on a monster of a barbecue overlooking beautiful Lake Merritt. (See the postcard in this group I have sent you. It is as thickly settled as in the picture!) A barge was moored on the west side of Lake Merritt opposite 13th Street holding what looked like about

COPYRIGHT 1908 BY C.H. JENSEN

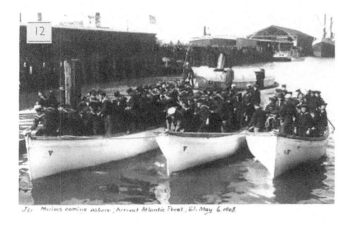

J.6, Marines coming ashore; Arrival Atlantic Fleet, S.F. May 6, 1908.

30,000 spectators surrounding the area. There were two huge tents erected for the cooks. Even the Oakland newspaper thought it a monster of a barbecue, and listed what was served: "One ton of dressed meats, 200 bulls heads, 7,000 loaves of bread, 50 sacks of potatoes to make potato salad, 600 gallons of coffee, 100 gallons of pure cream, 250 gallons of Mexican chili sauce, hundreds of pounds of cold meats of various kinds, over 3,000 apple pies, and great quantities of salt, pepper, butter and other articles." (113) There were over 100 waiters to serve all of us. While we enjoyed the barbecue, the officers dined in Piedmont Park. Later, when the food was cleared, Japanese citizens put on a firework display at the lake.

After the parade and dinner in the park, the officers attended another banquet in Oakland. I am uncertain where exactly but am thankful I did not have to attend. It duplicated San Francisco with the number of wines, courses, and speakers. I understand the only difference on the menu was the offering of martinis!

I will be meeting again with Frank tomorrow. It is late, or should I say early, so I'll close and write more later.

11 May

Dear Minnie,

Let me give you an update on the animals aboard our ships. I remember you asked about them in Los Angles, so I did a little investigating. I found out the two monkeys on board the *Louisiana* were discharged for bad behavior. It seems they were throwing everything they could lay their hands on out the port window of Lieutenant Evans' stateroom. At first, everything went well with the monkeys after they were brought on board from one of the South American countries. After we had sailed past Lima, rumor has it that Lieutenant Evans entered his room and watched a pair of his shoes and then a toothbrush sail out the porthole. The monkeys were put ashore. The *Louisiana* claims the largest number of pets on board. Hunter (one of the officers) has a thoroughbred French poodle named Pear. They are also very proud of the two parrots purchased in Trinidad. There are four other dogs owned by officers: Salty, Mutt, and Rummy, plus another bull terrier, and two cats.

Bill, the goat, resides on the *Vermont*. They tell me he's a fire-eater who eats burning cigarettes, cigars, and any other kind of hot ashes.

The *Kearsarge* acquired a monkey from Lima, Peru they named Tom. He is continually burning his fingers on the hot stove, so he has been barred from the galley. (114) They are also having trouble with the parrot they brought back from Trinidad. The bird only speaks Spanish and some broken English. When the sailors line up for inspection every morning, the parrot laughs and says, "Beat it," "Cut it out," and a few swear words which I can't write here. (115) To make matters worse, Tom doesn't like the parrot, so the two must be separated. The bird, however, has made friends with the captain's Scottish terrier.

The *Minnesota* has a pet raccoon. That animal always seems knows when payday comes and stands waiting for his sweets. No one has seen him for several days, however, so it's assumed the coon is either hibernating or has been stolen. Then again, like I said before, visitors take anything they can carry off the ship, so who knows.

Take care and I will write again when I get some free time.

Maurice

12 May

I have to tell you Min, we are really treated decently in San Francisco. When I ask for directions, a citizen gets out his official fleet program—which everyone seems to carry— and directs me to the location I need. I didn't feel the uniform had any respect while I was stationed on the East Coast; the people there were as frosty as their coldest winter day. Maybe the climate has something to do with temperament.

Minnie, let me give you an idea of the ever-present crowds of people. According to the paper, the evening the officers honored Secretary Metcalf, a 52-year old woman from Alameda drowned off the Mission Street wharf while looking at our illuminated battleships. She was pushed off the wharf by the crowds of people trying to get a better view! There were excursion boats for a price, just like in San Pedro, so people could sail out to view our ships at a closer distance. There was a sailor from one of the excursion boats who jumped in to try to save the lady, but he was unsuccessful. It looks like the woman didn't know how to swim. Get ready; I'm teaching you to swim next time we get together!

There are so many activities planned for us; I certainly won't have time to be bored. This will probably mean fewer problems for the Shore Patrol. There are school tours, and outings to Mt. Tamalpais, San Jose, and Oakland. We have daily athletic events with ribbons and awards given to the winners, chaperoned dances, and picnics . . . all of which aren't as much fun without you.

The officers had an opportunity to visit Yosemite, a place I would like to see with you.

As I wrote earlier, Frank arrived in time to see the parade and to take advantage of my extended leave. We each paid 10 cents to take a street car to China Town, Golden Gate Park, and see the construction beginning on the Cliff House. As you can see by the postals, this Cliff House was quite different from our Cliff Houses down home. The Cliff House in the enclosed postal burnt down 7 September 1907 after the earthquake. They are hoping to reopen sometime in 1909.

This area is quite beautiful, but I don't like the wind that comes through the Golden Gate. L. A. for mine, but won't say why! Don't you think Golden Gate Park is a pretty place? I like places when there is plenty of underbrush and no clay hills. I do so love flowers. I'd like to take just one little girl out for a stroll in a place so beautiful.

How do you like the postcard with the make-believe ship? Won't say which one I am. The ladies in this picture are all friends and relatives of a buddy of mine. I have enclosed several postals in this envelope, so the postman does not have a chance to read my messages. Be a good little girl, and I will send you something nice by and by.

The Embarcadero YMCA installed a Naval Clubhouse with pool tables, reading matter, and sobering-up services. Portraits of Admiral Evans were hung in all the saloons around town. "A few muted reports from police blotters indicated that the jacks weren't wholly engrossed in activities of such programmed innocence, but Edwardian taste kept coverage on these accounts restrained." (116) For eleven days and nights, the parties, dinners, luncheons, and picnics fell all over each other.

Your Sailor Boy Arrived O.K.

3043. The Cliff House and Seal Rocks, San Francisco

MAY 6th 08

SAN FRANCISCO

13 May 1908

Dear Minnie,

So how is my Little Girl today?

I wanted to write more than a few postcards to my sweet girl.

I must tell you about the automobile tour here in Frisco sponsored for us by the California State Auto Association. Tours began at 10:00 am on Monday, 11 May. There were enough observation cars donated for 250 men to leave the Ferry Building every 2 ½ hours to visit the city. *The San Francisco Examiner* donated fifty cars, and private citizens provided the rest. It was quite a riotous day. At one point, there were 238 cars all traveling together, spanning a total of two miles. All sightseeing with 2,000 of us Bluejackets, motoring at about fifty feet from one another. Well, it wasn't long before we started yelling for more speed. It became a free-for-all! Cars sometimes traveled four abreast racing down Ocean Avenue. (Was I on one of those cars???)

The owner of our automobile took our group home after the tour for a home-cooked meal and entertainment. It was very delightful. A home-cooked meal after surviving the ship's mess was a wonderful gift. Most of the men who were lucky enough to ride in a private car received similar treatment.

Yesterday, 12 May, was San Jose and Vallejo Day. You should have seen some of the officers when they arrived back aboard ship. Some of their faces appeared unrecognizable with the dust still visible from the roads. One dirty bunch of fellows, I tell you. They gladly related stories of their day. I'll try to put it all together for you:

There was an excursion by train to San Jose planned for 300 officers with a one-hour stopover to view Stanford University and then on to Santa Clara University. San Jose was the last stop, and it was packed with people all throwing flowers. One of the officers told us he was having a great time until some girl socked him in the eye with a bunch of roses. (117)

He went on to tell us the ride was so long and dusty that his fellow officers were afraid their uniforms would be forever ruined. All along the route, people waved flags. Somewhere between Stanford and Santa Clara, the train stopped, and ladies in white served the officers lemonade. While the gentlemen were out of the train cars enjoying their refreshments, they estimated about 5,000 children and women spent three hours decorating the cars with flowers the children had furnished. They decorated each passenger car with a different kind of flower: one car had sweet peas, another had roses, and one was covered with lilies. There were so many flowers, it was difficult to crawl back into the cars.

When the officers arrived at Santa Clara University, they were presented with a poem, or as Lt. Willing put it, ". . . everyone turned out with a band and some old bloke read a piece of poetry, but as there must have been 100 autos not many heard him." (118) Here is the poem that was presented:

WELCOME HEROES
by
MARLEN E. PEW.

I
A proud, though bloodless victory's won;
A feat attained; a service done.
The golden Western sun in glory gilds
The white ships that a mighty nation builds
    To shield us from the wolves of war.

II
The hemispheres that split the seas
Undaunt such splendid ships as these.
High on the masts the peace doves gladly ride,
But far o'erhead the screaming eagles glide,
    Assuring peace by show of power.

III
So tip the cup to Evans' crew;
The men in gold, the boys in blue.
A dozen thousand miles from coast to coast;
A brilliant proof—to all the world a boast
    Of strength of East and West alike.

23

WELCOME TO THE CAPTAINS OF THE FLEET

Heirs of heroes with whose glorious deeds our annals are replete, -

Freedom's warriors whose brave story knows nor shame nor base retreat, -

With the warmth of California hearts your noble band we greet!

Welcome thrice and three times o'er from bannered town and shouting street!

From our purple-fruited orchards, from our fields of golden wheat,

From our hills, where the Sequoias guard their kingdom's ancient seat,

Rolls the chorus of our welcomes, while glad hearts the measure beat,

And the roses of our vale are strewn a carpet for your feet!

Ye that on the wave triumphant bear Columbia's standard-sheet;

Ye, our pride in peace, our claim reliance still in battle's heat;

Ye, whom Triton love--the brave, to whom the land's acclaim is meet-

Santa Clara bids ye hail, and dips her pennant to THE FLEET!

Albert Shumate, M. D. (119)

There were about 500 men who also had the opportunity for an excursion by auto to Vallejo ending with an inter-squadron boat race in the afternoon. You know me, if I get a chance to ride in an automobile,

I take it. So, I went to Vallejo and was able to purchase a couple of postals for you. After the boat race, my buddies and me went to the reception and ball organized by the California Club.

24

17 May

Dear Minnie,

Well, we have a new admiral in command. Remember I told you Admiral Evans retired and the command was given to Admiral Thomas? On 15 May, the command was given to Admiral Sperry. Admiral Thomas didn't look all that well, anyway.

Frank will probably fill you in on the next few days when he gets home.

On 13 – 16 May, there were daily excursions for the men and their guests to journey up Mount Tamalpais and to Muir Woods. Frank was my guest, and we each paid $1.50 for the round trip on 13 May as I had duty on 15 and 16 May. I am sending you a postal of the train going up the mountain. The cars are all open, resembling a circus train.

It was so beautiful at the top of the mountain; I felt like a Roman gladiator observing Rome in the days of Caesar. But oh, what a difference in the morning up there. You would enjoy this trip! Only wish you had been here with Frank and me, but never mind. There will come a time some day soon. We enjoyed ourselves immensely at this famous resort. We hiked most of the day in areas I know you would have favored.

The only problem I am continually encountering with shore leave is the ladies who are constantly clawing at us as we come ashore. We have to hold tight to our caps and neckerchiefs. They all want souvenirs to take home and seem to stop at nothing to obtain a few. Each time a cap or neckerchief disappears it costs us an additional 25 cents when we board our respected ships.

Thursday, 14 May was Berkeley Day filled with athletic events and tours. We went to the University of California and sat in the Greek Theater. What a majestic outdoor amphitheater they have! After our tour, races were scheduled which I always enjoy. However, I must tell you by this time the special attention was wearing thin, and I began looking forward to things returning to normal.

We traveled to Santa Rosa on 16 May to march in yet another parade. We found vehicles decorated with Chinese and Japanese lanterns, and a rose float for the newly crowned Rose Carnival Queen and her family who paraded along with us. After this parade, a "battle of roses" took place in front of the courthouse, which brought back all the nightmarish memories of the Santa Barbara incident! You know I love flowers, Min, but this is going too far! After the parade, the Order of the Elks gave a luncheon for the officers while we were guests of the Women's Improvement Club.

Many of the officers and men elected to take the tour to Muir Woods and Mt. Tamalpais. There were enough cars for 25 officers and 175 enlisted men to tour the city of Santa Rosa. As I had already been to Mt. Tamalpais and Muir Woods with Frank, I elected for the tour of the city. Early that evening, Santa Rosa hosted a party for all 4,000 of us at the local theaters. Later that night, we were escorted back to ready our ships to steam to the state of Washington. I have made a promise to myself: to bring you to Frisco so you can share in the sights that so delighted Frank and me. What a wonderful time we will have.

Maurice

Two divisions of the fleet left San Francisco on 18 May at 1100 for Bellingham Bay, Washington arriving on Friday, 22 May. They remained close to shore, traveling at 13 knots so the crowds that had gathered could get a better view of the ships. The other division toured Puget Sound for a two-day visit, arriving on 21 May. Two of the battleships remained in the naval yard for repairs while the remaining fleet sailed into Seattle. The *Louisiana*, *Virginia*, *Ohio*, and *Wisconsin* visited Port Angeles, and the *Illinois* and *Kearsarge* visited Port Townsend. The *Maine* and the *Alabama* were officially detached from the Atlantic fleet on 18 May and were replaced by the *Nebraska* and *Wisconsin*. (120)]

WASHINGTON

Atlantic Fleet in Bellingham, Wash., Harbor, May 23, 1908. Said to be the finest Harbor in the World. *On tour around world*

8 July 1908

Dearest Minnie,

Now that we are once again under steam and heading toward Hawai'i, I have some badly needed time off to answer your kind letter I had received before we left Frisco. You always brighten my spirits with your long letters, thank you for your sweetness.

We left San Francisco on 18 May for Seattle. Two divisions took a detour and visited Bellingham Bay. Happily, I missed the main event of the two-day visit—the always tiring parade. There occurred a tragic event in Bellingham Bay, however. Two sailors from the *New Jersey*—Third-class Master-at-arms F. L. Lulinski and Seaman J. J. Staub, were crushed to death under the wheels of a Lake Whatcom streetcar. At about 1830, the two sailors— along with a coal passer, J.J. Kelly of the *New Jersey*, and another sailor from the *Vermont*— were riding on the front fender of the streetcar when the chain snapped and all the men were thrown to the ground. According to reports in the *Bellingham Herald*, the two on the outside of the streetcar were able to fall clear of the track, but Straub was not so lucky. The front wheel of the truck passed clear over Straub, killing him instantly. Lulinski was thrown between the wheels and dragged for a quite a distance before the streetcar was able to stop. (121) He died a few hours later at St. Luke's Hospital. The responsibility for the accident was placed solely on the sailors. I did not personally know these men, but I cannot help but feel the loss.

We arrived in Seattle on 23 May, anchoring four days. Even before we steamed into port, people began to arrive carrying hampers full of food hoping to reserve the best vantage point to view the fleet. By 1:00 pm, the better views had been taken and we could see thousands of people settling on the rooftops of hotels, restaurants, and businesses. We steamed into port at 2:00 pm.

When I received my leave, I went over to Bremerton to enjoy this grand work of nature. You can see by the five cards I have purchased for you how very impressed I am with this area. It also reminded me of the beauty of Frisco's Golden Gate Park. What is art compared to nature's beautiful handy work? Just think of our own pretty scenery, especially along the Old Cumberland River and Old Mill Creek. To my idea, this is the kind of place to repeat that famous of musical declarations, *The Sweetest Story Ever Told*. Please don't think me in the least sentimental, but now isn't this a lovely place? Remember that I am very fond of perusing lengthy missives and oblige! I am sending Frank some postals as well. Looking at all this grandeur, I am just thinking what fools we mortals be. Even though these beautiful hotels look inviting, a log shack for mine will seem proper after marching in yet another parade.

WELCOME TO OUR FLEET

SEATTLE
MAY 23-26

2

The *Seattle Star* reported, "From Peak to peak waved the long streamers of signal flags, a kaleidoscope of color, and the suggestion of death which lurked in the mouths of the huge runs that stared out of the main deck turrets were softened by the cloak of white paint, representing the errand of peace upon which the great fleet had entered in its around-the-world cruise." (122)

"The cruise of this enormous sea fighting force is pronounced by the European and Asiatic observers to be the greatest diplomatic stroke of the century and the strongest influence exerted in recent years for world peace." (123) The official program was given to the officers so they would be prepared for the many receptions and dinners that followed. The entertainment was as full in Seattle as it had been in San Francisco.

BATTLESHIP FLEET ENTERING SEATTLE HARBOR   855

The senior officers were met with autos at Pier 6 and taken to Snoqualmie Falls. The Seattle physicians held an informal smoker at the "Perry" to entertain the surgeons of the fleet. The *Virginia* and the *Louisiana* hosted a tour for the school children on 25 May. During the short stay, sports events were scheduled every day, and free theater tickets were issued to the enlisted men while the officers were saddled with numerous teas and receptions.

Minnie, I thought you would enjoy the story of the newest addition to our growing menagerie; a bear cub has been presented to each ship! I am sending along the clipping that appeared in the paper because I couldn't describe it any better. "Sixteen live bears is a unique sight in any barroom, and though small, the future mascots for Uncle Sam's fighting machines made things exceedingly lively in that section of the house where the Butler patrons (of the Butler Bar and Grill), imbibe their liquid refreshments. Bang went a table as one particularly lively specimen of bear tribe waddled around and caught its chain about the table leg. There was a clatter and crash and a shower of broken glass as the tray smashed to the floor.

"The success of the bears in the future years and prosperity and honor for the ships and crews to which they have attached their homage was pledged in a round of sparkling wine, and as if enthused by the sentiment proposed, several cubs emitted a healthy-lunged howl. Aboard the ships all was in readiness to receive the mascots. On the *Kansas*, Bruinski, as their specimen was immediately christened, took firm hold of the situation by whipping all the dogs and cats aboard.

"The *Connecticut's* teddy, once aboard, had a row with the goat and the pig, taking his claim as the new mascot. On the *Minnesota*, a green parrot and a brown monkey greeted the new teddy. The parrot didn't like the bear at all, and voiced his disapproval in language that would have not sounded nice in the presence of ladies. The monkey gave a squeal, grabbed a bunch

(left) Photo: NH 50480 *USS Missouri* (Battleship # 11) Bear cub presented to the ship by the Citizens of Seattle, Washington, 1908. *U.S. Naval History and Heritage Command Photograph.*

of bear hide and dashed away with a big tuft of wool sticking out from behind his fingers." (124) I wish I could have been there, what a sight this must have been! Min, these little guys look like small puppies, each one only weighing around nine pounds. Of course, I'm sure they won't stay that size for long. I can tell you, our goat is not happy to share the spotlight with this small but loud bag of fur.

The parade in Seattle took place on 26 May to celebrate the last day of our visit. The newspaper claimed it was the "Greatest Parade in the history of the city." (125) I am wondering if my feet will hold out until the end of the cruise. This parade was huge with the paper estimating some 15,000 were in the procession, and about 400,000 spectators from Washington, Oregon, Idaho, Montana, and British Columbia were on hand to view the pageant. Each company was greeted with a wave of cheers and a shower of flowers as we passed the officers in the reviewing stands. (What is it about showers of flowers after each parade?) All along the route was strewn Washington's state flower, the Rhododendron. And of course, our newly acquired sixteen Harbor bear cubs were in the parade immediately following our division. The paper said this about us: "A brave array they made, these sturdy sons of ours, clothes in the nation's uniform of blue; a living tide of valor enrolled under the starry flag of freedom and sanctified in the fires of a liberty which has lighted the world, ennobled in generous deed and creased with the colors of a hero nations." (126)

On 27 May, the fleet divided. My new division, the Third, along with the First Division, returned to Hunters Point, San Francisco with the First Division first making a brief overnight stop

The Naval Parade at Seattle, Washington, May 26, 1908.

at Tacoma. The Fourth Division made a three-day visit to Tacoma before going to Bremerton, Washington for repairs.

After our return to Frisco, our time was filled with coaling, taking on supplies, and repainting—readying our ships for the long journey to Hawai'i. We also received some new midshipmen from the Naval Academy to replace the 129 men who deserted.

The announcement was made during this time that the fleet would return to Hampton Roads on Washington's Birthday, 22 February 1909, so we could complete the tour before President Roosevelt left office.

As you know, Min, there were wives who have followed their officer husbands all along the coast of California. Well, they were not willing to give their men up again. The ladies hired a luxury liner, the *Bremen*— a North German liner— to follow the fleet as best as possible. The women are planning to meet their husbands in Honolulu, Sydney, Tokyo, and the Riviera so they can attend as many balls and receptions as possible. Needless to say, the officers are not happy about the situation, but the ladies had already hired the liner, so there wasn't much they could do about it.

On 4 July, some of us went back to Lake Merritt in Oakland to see the fireworks celebration. It was well worth the effort. I so wish you and Frank could have joined me. The fireworks were spectacular to see. Those on the *Vermont* had to stay behind because they were hosting a farewell reception on her main deck. We heard all about it when we returned to the *Virginia*.

Special tugs had been chartered to ferry guests to the *Vermont*. The remaining Bluejackets escorted the guests to a canopy on the decorated forecastle. The guns were elevated high above the people, and a stage was erected for the presentation of a program. My buddies on the *Vermont* told me it was quite an event. The band played sentimental songs, waltzes, as well as Irish instrumental dance music: jigs, reels, and hornpipes. The Green Mountain Quintet sang ragtime songs, and there was even a violin solo. Boxing bouts were scheduled after the music. When the entertainment was over, the guests were escorted around the deck to the refreshments that had been prepared by the Athletic Association. The finale was a grand ball and a band concert all of which occurred while I was thoroughly enjoying myself and relaxing in Oakland.

We began steaming for Hawai'i yesterday at 2:00pm. While we were preparing to leave, the *Connecticut* received one more animal to take aboard. Someone told a Miss Herrscher the sailors on board the *Connecticut* were upset because the other ships had an Angora goat and they didn't. So, she took an Angora goat with gilded horns from her estate in San Leandro and presented it to

the *Connecticut* as a mascot from San Francisco!

Before I close this letter, I want to once again tell you how much your long letters mean to me, how much they lift my spirits and give me a ray of hope for future encounters. This will have to be mailed as soon as we reach Hawai'i. I was able to mail some more postcards before we upped anchor, however.

With best regards to my gal,

Maurice

Sailors' Parade, Tacoma, Washington, May 27th. 2528

Every American who viewed the spectacular show of power by the fleet "felt complete confidence that the United States could lick any other country in the world, and if necessary, the world itself." (127) The total entertainment cost for San Francisco was $70,990.56. When the fleet took their leave, there was a surplus of $4,468.57 in their budget, 6% of the amount of the total amount collected. This excess money was voted to be given to the many bands that had performed during the fleet's visit and to be used to upgrade the naval club. (128)

A badly needed hospital ship, the *Relief*, joined the fleet with its new medicines and physicians. Most naval men had previously declared the *Relief* to be unseaworthy. She had begun in the harbors of New York as a Long Island Ferry and could perform coastal duties well, but she was not equipped for a lengthy cruise. The *Relief* was originally scheduled to sail with the fleet from Hampton Roads, but there had been a problem with command. Roosevelt wanted to choose a civilian, the Navy wanted a Naval officer. Roosevelt won, and the Surgeon Charles F. Stokes became the commander of the hospital ship. The *Relief* was a welcome sight when it arrived in San Francisco. "Two insane men, two consumptives, two cases of paralysis, and a few others were transferred to the hospital ship. A total of 152 ailing crewmembers of the fleet were eventually taken aboard the *Relief* and conveyed to the naval hospital at Mare Island, California", a two-hour trip away. (129) There were several cases of scarlet fever and diphtheria on the *Nebraska*. The ship was placed in quarantine at Angel's Island to be fumigated. She was cleared two days later and joined the fleet in the Pacific on 15 July.

Two casualties clouded the celebrations on the West Coast. Captain Henry McCrea died from Bright's disease on 20 July, and two captains were fired for their supposed laziness. Reporters Robert Jones and Franklin Matthews remained on the cruise while nine other journalists were asked to be relieved of their duties because their reports did not comply with the regulations that Roosevelt had set up ahead of the cruise.

The six torpedo boats had proved to be unseaworthy in the first part of the voyage. A decision was made to have eight armored cruisers of the Pacific fleet tow the torpedo boats to Samoa for repairs, then wait for the fleet to reach Japan.

Admiral Sperry was still concerned about a rumored sea attack by Japan. Once again, he asked Roosevelt about changing the color of the ships to gray. Once again, he was refused. As soon as the fleet left San Francisco for Hawai'i, Sperry had the division spread out beam to beam to save coal by not steaming in each other's wake. Because the *Nebraska* and the *Wisconsin* had replaced the *Maine* and the *Alabama*, Sperry brought the prettiest and newest ships up front, thus changing the divisions and their replacements. He ordered the fleet to practice all kinds of maneuvers including the "S" formation to be used when visiting foreign ports. Sperry commanded the crews to work hard, to become more professional. In return, he gained their respect.

As the fleet was under way, the Japanese newspapers were printing untrue articles about all the thousands of sailors who had deserted in every California port. The Japanese hoped this kind of reporting would handicap the fleet's operation in the Pacific.

21 July 1908

Dear Min,

I was so delighted to finally hear from you. Your dear letters cause me to feel that you are growing in my purest esteem. Thank you for the treasured photo of you that you sent in this letter. It will be safe in my ditty box where I can look at it while I write to you.

I found this postal while in Frisco and decided to add it to this letter. The *Glacier* is the most important factor in the cruise. She carries our grub and supplies, and our combined meat, grocery, and candy store. We couldn't do without her.

We learned only a few days ago that Admiral Thomas died of a heart attack on 3 July. If you remember, I told you when he stepped down from his command that he didn't look too healthy to me.

The next portion of this cruise is all very new to me. Hawai'i is a place we have only recently heard about, and few have visited. I will try to detail our visit as best as possible so you can share it with Frank.

Thank goodness we had a very uneventful voyage from San

Francisco! We arrived in Hawai'i on 16 July. Before steaming into Honolulu, we took a short detour to sail past the island of Moloka'i to give the estimated 1,200 people of the leper colony a chance to view the fleet. From the deck of our ship, we could see these people really appreciated the extra effort we took to put on a display for them.

Our division— the *Louisiana, Missouri, Ohio* and *Virginia*— went to Lahaina on the Island of Maui to coal because of the underdeveloped facilities at Pearl Harbor. Only the *Connecticut* and one other division were able to enter Pearl Harbor. The rest of the ships had to anchor outside the breakwater waiting their turn to coal at O'ahu.

When our division arrived in Lahaina, people lined the shores flying American flags; all around us came the sound of fireworks. We were told about two-thirds of the population of Maui are Japanese who work on sugar plantations. These people created a giant welcome screen of bamboo on the waterfront. As soon as we were able to come ashore, a luau was prepared with lots of dancing and singing of Hawaiian melodies on native instruments. You would have enjoyed this, Min. The flow of the music is nothing like our familiar melodies. The musicians were very interesting to observe. They were all playing by ear; none of them could read a note of music that I could see. What a talent! Our short stay here was so low-key. We surely needed the break from our constant activity, chores, and drilling.

I heard later that thousands of people in Honolulu greeted the other divisions, lining the shore and atop Diamond Head Mountain. Many decorated steamers loaded with well-

SOUVENIR MAP
SHOWING THE ROUTE TAKEN
BY THE ATLANTIC FLEET
FROM HAMPTON ROADS TO
HONOLULU. HAWAII. U. S. A.

2

Nothing in sight for days, but 16 ships and the horizon.

3

Sailors Parade At Honolulu, Hawaiian Islands, July 1908.

wishers also sailed out to greet the ships. Because this is an American territory, there were no national salutes fired. (130) The reception in Honolulu was as quiet, and low key as ours had been in Lahaina. They were given no real itinerary, just two or three scheduled formal dinners for the admirals and captains.

The day after the ships landed in Honolulu, the men had to once again march in a parade, poor souls. Because the people had read about our marching in Santa Barbara with flowers in our rifles, the Hawaiian women wanted the men to march in their pageant with flower garlands, called lei, around their necks, but this was not agreeable with the Admirals.

So, the men marched without lei, but the route was strewn with flowers and people tossed wreaths at the men, throwing their hats off balance. As a compromise, I'm told, there were about 100 ladies on the landing stage at the end of the parade giving out lei to the sailors as they completed their march. (132)

We didn't join the rest of the divisions in Honolulu until 19 July. What a treat for us. That meant we were too late to march in the parade! So, we were free to come and go as we pleased. The Hawaiian men are quite handsome, but for the most part, I would have to say the women are a bit too fat but very hospitable.

The ex-governor, George Carter, who was in charge of the reception committee wrote to President Roosevelt on 13 July, - - - "Every man of the fleet who parades on Friday next must yield to the Hawaiian custom and accept a wreath of flowers as a token of their regard for the navy - - " (131)

The Navy officials said no to this request. They wanted the men to march as a navy should march so the foreign countries would view the navy as a strong disciplined force.

The folks at home have just received a set of Comic Naval Post Cards, sent them by a sailor of Admiral Evan's Fleet.

I went to the Bishop Museum as you see by the enclosed postal. I wrote some of these cards during my tour of the city. The aquarium is the finest I have ever seen. Hawai'i is a gorgeous land with all kinds

of tropical vegetation growing everywhere and the temperature around 80 degrees every day with just a slight ocean breeze. I only wish I was with the one girl in this world for me. Look at the card of Washington Place, the ex-Queen Liliʻuokalani's Home in Honolulu. How would this place suit you for a home? I was also able to go horseback riding again, and I tested the water for a delightful swim at Waikiki. Of course, I did some hiking through some of the beautiful scenery. Won't you come and go for a swim with me in these warm waters? Can't swim? As I said before, we'll just have to take care of that when I see you again!

Washington Place, Ex-Queen Lilinkalani's Home, Honolulu, J. H.

All of our entertainment was sponsored by the sugar growers because the Polynesians secluded themselves and the queen had fled to Lahaina, refusing to participate in any of the celebrations. (133) There were more teas and dances than originally scheduled because the officers' wives, who had joined us from their steamer, wanted to reciprocate the Hawaiians generosity. Every evening, the Moana and the Seaside Hotels had open balls and entertainment for the men. The officers were entertained at the most prominent building in the city, the Alexander Young

Ex-Queen Lilinkalani, Honolulu, J. H.

Americans had little knowledge about the Hawaiian Islands and its people before the arrival of the fleet. Families back home were quickly informed about the new territory through letters and postcards that described the region, its climate, culture, and vegetation. Maurice certainly did his part.

Hotel. It's six stories high with a roof garden at either end. The roof itself is about 1/2 an acre! We all received coconuts, sugar cane, pineapples, and bananas as gifts. The last night we were in port, every hotel had a dance, our ships were all illuminated, and fireworks lit the sky; a truly magical evening.

Moana Hotel, Honolulu, T. H.

23 July

We are scheduled to leave Honolulu tonight at 6:00 pm. The *Minnesota* is to remain behind to retrieve the mail that is late in arriving. This will be our longest run. It is 3,850 miles to our next port in New Zealand, and our decks are stacked with bags of coal for the expected use. Our first-class ship, the *Virginia*, won't have a problem with

the long cruise or the extra coal consumption because of our larger bunker capacity. However, some of the battleships will need to be very creative in their coal use to be able to stretch their allotment that far.

Please write as often as you can, for in the treasure of my heart you hold a most sacred place. Be good, Little Girl, until I come home.

Yours,

Maurice

The only significant engineering problem during the cruise occurred while in Honolulu. On 18 July, a steam pipe in the *Kearsarge* broke, injuring five enlisted men. It took nine hours to be fully operable. (134)

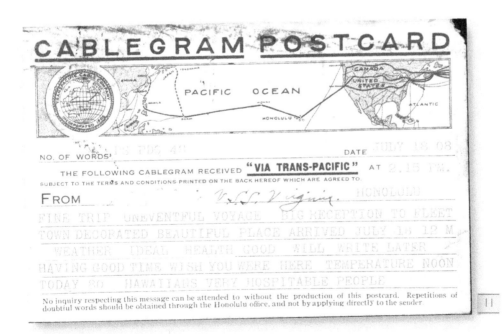

AUCKLAND, NEW ZEALAND

While steaming toward New Zealand, the ships continued to practice their fancy maneuvers in preparation for the display to be given for the British. When the navy talked about impressing the world, the number one country on their list was Great Britain. But the drill got out of hand one day as the *New Jersey* steamed into line a bit too close astern of the *Nebraska*. The *New Jersey* rammed the bow, going through the battleship into the Surgeon's room. The details however, were kept a secret. The *Nebraska* made the necessary repairs and continued on the cruise.

Saturday, 1 August 1908

Dearest Minnie,

As luck would have it, 28 July the entire fleet halted temporarily in mid-ocean while the *Minnesota* rejoined the formation to disperse the long-awaited mail. Included was a letter from my dear sweet girl. So, you can see how important your letters are to me.

Yours is the one sweet name that causes my heart to long for the future. I'm feeling very lonely today, and writing to you lifts my spirits.

You probably know by looking at the postal map I sent you, we

crossed the equator again. The ceremonies were duplicated for the new recruits who had joined us in San Francisco. This time Doctor Pills, who cures all ills, Uncle Sam, and Miss Columbia performed the ceremony. It is always asked of each man, "Will you take your medicine or pay the fine?" Of course, everyone replied,

"Yes, we will take the medicine." Well, the first to be summoned by King Neptune this time was Teddy Virginia, our bear cub! Unfortunately, no one understood his answer to that question, and after a shave, over he went into the awaiting tank. He was still crying half an hour later, but I'm sure he's glad to become a shellback with the rest of us. Ha, ha! (135)

Recreation and Stag "Hop" on board a U. S. Battleship.

To ease the boredom on this long voyage, our brass band— of which I'm a part— entertained on the quarterdeck. Group singing, fencing contests, boxing bouts, and plays were also available diversions.

10 August

The closer we got to New Zealand, the more wintry and chilly it became. The uniform of the day was once again changed to our warmer blue. I have to remember the seasons in the southern hemisphere are the opposite of what we are used to up north. While you're enjoying summer, it's late autumn down here. The run was very smooth for the most part until 4 August when we encountered rough seas for four days—no boredom then, not even a chance to write! You should have seen our hospital ship, the *Relief*, rolling about fifty-five degrees through the high seas.

Since the departure from San Francisco, the hospital ship, the *Relief*, encountered numerous misfortunes. "Her refrigeration system broke down en route to Hawai'i, resulting in the loss of all her frozen stores." (136) During the rough seas steaming to Auckland, "it was only with difficulty that patients were kept in their bunks." (137)

U.S. Fleet entering Auckland Harbour, square. Arrived 9th, 1908

Auckland, from St. Matthew's Tower

This entrance was captured on a stereopticon slide to become a best seller: "Sixteen engines backed and stopped, sixteen anchors plunged, sixteen jacks caught the wind and sixty-four guns opened saluting" (139) to the enjoyment of the 100,000 people who lined the beach.

Early Sunday morning, 9 August, we increased our speed to 13 knots to throw spray on the bows, reassembled in the single file "S" formation, and dropped anchor at 7:10 am— all except the *Rhode Island*. Finding insufficient room for her anchorage, she nearly rammed the British flagship, *Powerful*. The *Rhode Island* had to be taken to an alternate anchorage by the harbormaster. (138)

12 August

Minnie, Auckland was truly in a holiday spirit when we arrived. All blue laws, normally in force on Sunday, as well as the Parliament in Wellington, were suspended. Once again, men, women, and children covered the shores by the thousands, (140) all throwing their hats in the air and waving handkerchiefs. When we came ashore, they all wanted to shake our hands.

Blue Laws: a law prohibiting certain activities such as entertainment, trading or leisure activities on Sunday.

The city was decorated the likes not seen before on this cruise. American flags and flowery arches adorned Queen Street—one of the main thoroughfares of Auckland. In the center of the arches that spanned the roadway, hung welcome signs written in the local languages and English, illuminated with electric lights.

Poles, decorated with shields and surrounded by national flags with a coat of arms of the United States, Great Britain, the Dominion and the City of Auckland, lined both sides of the street at prescribed intervals. Buildings in every direction displayed "Welcome" and "Hail Columbia" signs.

Friday, 14 August

At 8:00 pm the first evening in Auckland, illuminated the skies with our searchlights. Afterward, we were entertained with a full hour of fireworks from shore.

Speeches, dinners, dances, garden parties, receptions, and a ball at the governor's house had been planned, as well as our usual parade. These activities continued night and day. Admiral Sperry gave no fewer than eight speeches every day we were there. There was even a tree-planting ceremony in which sixteen trees were planted in Albert Park, representing each one of our battleships.

I didn't attend many of the planned functions but rather spent time exploring the beautiful countryside. Min, this is a beautiful country. How I wish you were here to share it with me. I visited two extinct volcanoes, Mount Eden and One Tree Hill, and delighted in the wonderful view they afforded me. I also visited the famous government owned Rotorua thermal springs and learned a little about the natives, the Māori's. I walked around boiling mud pools and watched cooking demonstrations by the natives. My postals tell more of a story about these people than I can write in words.

There don't appear to be any millionaires or apparent poverty here. When I asked, I was told the government seizes large estates and divides them up so no one is without. Not a bad idea, no?

Every night we've been in port, Queen Street has been so blocked with people that all vehicle and tramcar traffic has been suspended. (141) It was almost as crowded during the day making it difficult to get around.

We rode to the horse races in tramcars that were specially decorated for us, and then served a luncheon afterward. Such beautiful

Reception to the American Fleet at Auckland, New Zealand, Aug. 9th, 1908.

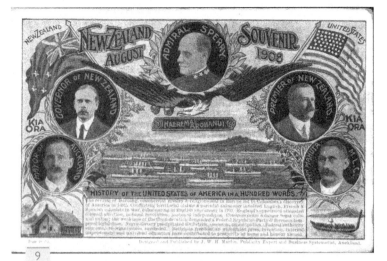

horses, but of course, Kentucky takes them all!

Today was our last day in port, and it's visitor's day for the citizens to come aboard. This time, the *Louisiana* played host while the rest of us finished coaling. We didn't complete the job until 11:00 o'clock. I have just had a wash. I believe you would have thought me a Negro had you seen me! (143) We saw thousands come to shore and sing "Auld Lang Syne" to us until the last liberty party had started for their ships. Two large decorated war canoes with warriors circled the fleet, hailing each vessel in their native tongue as the last of the men came aboard. We all agreed this was a beautiful spot for a short visit.

"Over 40,000 postcards were mailed from a special Queen Street Post Office open only to the sailors..." (142)

Please send me a little love; I need it so much. Always thinking of my one dear girl.

I must close with a loving request in hopes that you will accept. My dearest, it would make so happy if you would agree to be my wife at the end of my tour of duty. I love you dearly.

Your boy,

Maurice

All was not bliss that last night. The Shore Patrol had a battle with the sailors who had decided to remain in Auckland and not continue on the cruise. The Shore Patrol became so rough with some of the men, the citizens took the side of the deserters and attacked the patrol. They liberated many of the sailors.

Saturday, 15 August, the fleet departed for Australia at 8:00 am with two New Zealander recruits from Auckland.

Australia Welcomes America

Australia Welcomes America

Two weeks before the fleet arrived in Sydney, false rumors circulated once again about the murderous crimes committed by the terrible men aboard the Atlantic fleet. The source of these rumors was unknown, but they always preceded the fleet before their arrival.

20 August 1908

Dearest,

The seeming awkwardness in some people is a lack of personal experience, don't you think? I surrendered to you many days ago, now how about you? As you know, suspense has killed many people. I'm crazy to know your answer. If love be food for the conscience, then give me access to it. Suspense is terrible. Many thanks for the pretty card and long letter, though it I am still longing for the one answer I desperately seek.

Please pardon my seeming neglect in not writing sooner. Let me explain. The trip to Sydney was one I won't forget for a long while. It became quite stormy and very cold. By 19 August, the storm was raging so fiercely that we couldn't use our mess. We had to sit cross-legged on the deck holding on to our plates to keep our food from racing across the deck. (144) Just trying to get from one place to another on the ship was an adventure.

Passing the galley, I could see kettles sliding across the range and down onto the deck, leaving their contents in every direction, it was interesting to say the least. (145) Our poor bear cub had a most difficult time trying to get any sleep; every time he closed his eyes, he would slide to and fro. In our canteen— where things like cakes, jellies, candies, canned goods and special treats are sold— the entire store lay in a heap on the deck. (146)

One of my shipmates discovered a leak had sprung directly over his hammock when he felt drops of water on his face while trying to sleep. He finally moved to one of the storerooms on deck to get some relief, only to have a tall bottle of ink fall on him from a top shelf and completely paint his face! (147) This storm was recorded in the ship's log as a "choppy sea," not a "rough sea." I sure hope I'm fortunate enough never to experience a "rough sea." As we neared Sydney, the sea did calm a little and we had several large whales accompany us, blowing streams of water into the air. A truly delightful experience.

An hour and a half before our arrival, we heard a continuous discharge of fireworks. On closer look, we saw the illuminations exploding at a great height displaying Union Jacks, balloons, banners, birds, lanterns, balls, toys, willow trees, dragons, fish, animals, thunder clouds, elephants, camels, lions, golden rams, and grotesque figures. And this was a daylight display!

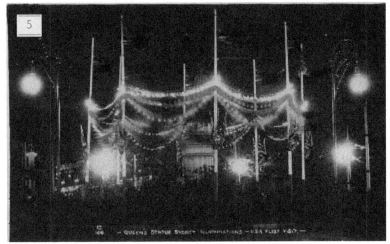

There were so many steamers and other craft dressed with flags to greet us, it looked like the beginning of a yacht race. We entered Botany Bay, at 9:00 am on 20 August and gave our usual 21-gun salute. We headed back out to the ocean and performed a square maneuver, and then returned to the harbor entrance. Once we dropped anchor, we saw thousands upon thousands of people on the bluffs.

Sydney is about half as large as San Francisco, but it looked like there were three times as many people greeting us that day. Every where we looked, there appeared to be a band playing the "Star Spangled Banner." The next day, the local paper estimated there were 500-650,000 people stretching 14 miles, who had been outside all night wrapped in blankets waiting for us. The article went on to say our arrival marked the biggest National celebration that Australia has ever held. It looks like Sydney was working to outdo Frisco and Auckland put together!

Official greetings were made, after which the admirals and commanding officers spent the first evening at the Government House for a formal dinner to begin the scheduled entertainment.

Many of my buddies have gone ashore to attend theaters and public and private parties this evening, but I preferred to stay aboard. I was able to get a full view of another hour and a half of fireworks from shore, which began around 8 pm. That also gave me the opportunity to write to you. There were so many rockets; there must have been 500 of dazzling whiteness, then another 500 rockets of colored stars, then all of them forming a bouquet of probably

1,000 rockets, from central stations (148) What a sight to behold!

I must close to be ready for our parade tomorrow.

Lovingly,

Maurice

25 August

Dearest,

As I mentioned earlier, our parade was scheduled on the first full day in port, 21 August. It was good to get it out of the way at the beginning of our visit. There was discussion back and forth before the parade; Sydney wanted us to march without our rifles, but Admiral Sperry objected, and rightly so. We would look a bit foolish, and he felt our hands needed to be occupied because the men would want to throw kisses to all the pretty girls watching our parade. (149) I know of some men who probably would have done just that! I wouldn't have been among them.

We marched through a series of plastic arches, each topped with a model of an American battleship, a welcome sign, or a picture of George Washington or President Roosevelt. A papier-mâché of the *Mayflower* hid the Custom House, and a replica of the Statue of Liberty stood five stories high in front of the newspaper office. Our Stars and Stripes were seen everywhere, and the parade route was jammed with people. After the parade was over, a luncheon was furnished for us at the Town Hall.

When I finally took my shore leave, I was amazed how much the area reminded me of Boston with the rolling wooded hills, crooked streets, and comfortable homes. This city looks more like our cities than any I have seen on this tour. The people are very courteous, and because English is spoken here, I felt like I was home. I think the most spectacular decorations were the buntings. They were composed of flags, hangings, and wood plaster banners that enclosed whole streets. Flags, flowers, and gold-painted plaster eagles were placed on every lamppost. I saw red, white, and blue everywhere. Why even waitresses in restaurants were wearing our colors. The newspaper claimed they spent $50,000 on those decorations! The Avenue of Pitt, one of the larger streets in the city, was renamed American Avenue for the week during the celebrations.

The day following the parade, I was able to take one of the daily railway excursions to the Jenolan Caverns. Every township along our route had decorations, and it appeared as if the town's entire population cheered as we passed. Looking at the cards I have selected, how would you like to be here? I enjoyed the forty-six acres of the botanical gardens and the zoological gardens. There was a mob of kangaroos and wallabies, as well as many other tree marsupials.

It would have taken days to see everything, but you get an idea from the postcards. I also took an excursion to the Blue Mountains. The waterfalls were beautiful, truly an area you would enjoy visiting. There are so many pretty scenes in L.A. that you will have to show

It needs to be remembered, Australia thought America was coming to support them. According to one source, Australia and New South Wales wanted to keep their country an all-white man's country. They dreaded what seemed to be the indifference of their home country, and they feared there would be an influx of people from Asia because of their need for more settlers. Australia was hopeful this visit by the fleet would awaken in Americans the beauty of their country, encouraging American immigrations to Australia.

me. Won't it be so fine to stroll out in the evening and hear good music and chat away to our hearts' content?

Once again, I am grateful to not be an officer. I heard one of the officers complain that he had to listen to twenty speeches given at a dinner he attended. He further complained that the Australians seemed to have a habit of making speeches whenever they had a chance, and many times when they hadn't been scheduled to do so. (150) Admiral Sperry alone sometimes gave as many as thirteen speeches in one day!

Some of the activities planned were very interesting to attend. There were contests in boomerang throwing, buck jumping, sheep shearing, wood chopping, and sheep dog trials. (151) How's *that*

for an afternoon of entertainment? As you can see I will have much to share when I return.

I must close but will write again once we set sail.

Your boy,

Maurice

Some of the wives who arrived on the *Bremen* were given free rooms in royal suites at major hotels, royal box seats at the opera, and many invitations. The wives were almost more popular than the fleet itself. The prettiest of the wives adorned postcards issued by the government and newspapers interviewed them daily for their opinions.

Walter Barnett, Photo.   Admiral Sperry passing The Exchange, Sydney.   Cooper, Sydney

SAILORS EXCURSIONS TO BLACK HEATH,
AUSTRALIA, IN THE BLUE MOUNTAINS
75 MILES INLAND FROM SIDNEY, AUGUST 22, 1908.

28, August

Dearest Minnie,

The last day in Sydney, 26 August, was quite a celebration. Our official photographers took many photographs, so I am sure you'll see the pictures of the pageant. There was a demonstration by 9,000 school children, to an audience of 75,000 on the cricket grounds, so claims the newspaper. Those children created living flags of two nations and sang "Hail Columbia," "Star Spangled Banner," and "God Save the Queen" as the 'flags' waved. Afterward, there were rifle matches, baseball games, and a garden party. It was the *Connecticut's* turn to host a dinner party on board that evening. (152) I had wondered before I arrived here if I would like Australians. I can tell you there was no doubt of my feelings when I departed.

372.
MAYPOLE DANCE.
FLEET CELEBRATIONS

Well Min, before we left, the fleet was presented with yet another animal. The *Connecticut* received her own wallaby. It'll be interesting to see how she fares with the bear cub as we travel. We left Sydney on 27 August at 8:00 am, accompanied by a large passenger steamer filled with sightseers. It's only a 600-mile run to Melbourne, but I wish it were longer so I could recuperate from all the festivities. I'm pretty worn out.

How I long for the time to come when I'm speeding as fast as the train can carry me to meet my one dear girl. Be a good girl, and I'll send you something nice by and by.

I pray your answer arrives soon so my heart will be lifted.

Maurice

When at Sydney, Admiral Sperry ordered the hospital ship, the *Relief* to go directly to Manila with the *Yankton* as an escort. After further inspection, it was decided the *Relief* would need to go home via Hawai'i and join the Pacific Fleet. The ship, under the command of a civilian doctor, decided to begin the journey after typhoon warnings had been posted. After many mishaps, the *Relief* managed to return to Manila. She was then declared unseaworthy and ordered to remain in Manila as a stationary hospital ship.

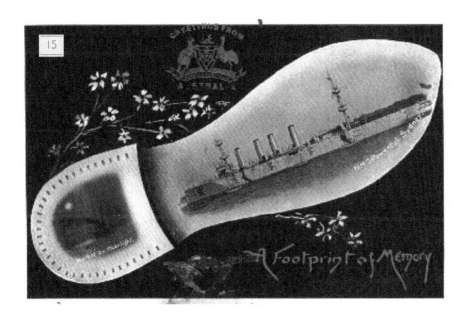

MELBOURNE, AUSTRALIA

The fleet's arrival in Melbourne on Saturday, 29 August at 3:00 pm was somewhat bungled. The speed they were traveling was too swift. When the order came to 'drop anchor and full steam astern' the battleships went astern, dropping fathom upon fathom of cable. "The *Nebraska* ran out 91 fathoms--it had been calculated that 45 fathoms would be ample, and then the might strain of the engines upon the cable discovered a link weaker than the rest and the cable parted." The *Nebraska* dropped her starboard bow anchor, "and the huge vessel rode motionless upon the waters." (153) Four of the ships got carried away when the first anchors dropped and cruised on toward the crowded docks, just missing the spectators.

The fleet arrived with forty-two bags of mail containing letters and postcards to be mailed back to the United States. On 3 September, the ship *S.S. Marama* sailed for Vancouver carrying "316 bags of mail matter, which included 112,326 letters and post-cards" from the fleet. (154) Collecting of postcards had become very popular for the men as well as for those back home. "Americans have one weakness common to men and officers—it is the craze for collecting post-cards. In all parts of the world the Americans have bought post-cards, and they show their collections with pardonable pride. All around the lower decks the marines could be seen with boxes unlocked, revealing treasured post-cards to admiring eyes." (155)

3 September 1908

Dearest,

I am writing to Frank today as well, poor lonesome guy. But he must get used to it, eh? I fear to hear from you again to know your answer. I can only hope that I may be in your thoughts as you are in mine.

When we arrived in Melbourne, we had to dock quite a ways from land. Our first job, as always, was to clean the sides of our ship. But sightseeing boats swarmed all around us. I lost track of how many of these boats had bands aboard, all playing the "Star Spangled Banner." It was tough to get our work completed, Minnie, for every time one of the bands came near our ship we had to stop what we were doing and stand at attention. It is interesting to listen to our national anthem being played by the Australians. They seem to play it like a jig at a pace that sounds like they want to get through it in a hurry, almost an allegro tempo. There also doesn't seem to be any dynamics or pauses; it becomes

almost unrecognizable. I will demonstrate when I see you again.

To reach the city, we are ferried for thirty minutes in a steamer to a landing in Williamstown, and then we walk a mile to the railroad station, and ride a train for another 45 minutes!

SOUVENIR OF UNITED STATES FLEET'S VISIT TO AUSTRALIA

1908

FLINDERS STREET, MELBOURNE.

AUSTRALIA WELCOMES THE FLEETS

WITH COMPLIMENTS—From TYE & CO. PROP. LTD., House Furnishers.
OUR ADDRESSES ARE:—
100-108 Bourke Street, MELBOURNE.   320-326 Chapel Street, PRAHRAN.   83-89 Swan Street, RICHMOND.
237-239 Smith Street, FITZROY.   405-407 Sydney Road, BRUNSWICK.   226-232 Clarendon Street, SOUTH MELBOURNE.

As I mentioned before, first class 'special' men are given shore leave whenever their work is completed. First class are given leave in sections, and the rest of the men have a poor chance of going ashore—the fourth class having no chance at all. It really is a shame there are quite a number of sailors who have not been ashore since the ships left Honolulu. (156) When I went ashore on Sunday, I spent the day getting acquainted with the city and buying the postcards I have enclosed. I was also able to get some free ones as well as the writing paper that I am using now at the Temperance Hall. Melbourne must have had fair warning of our letter writing activities, for they set up a new post office just for our use.

I find Melbourne's decorations similar to the last two cities, just not as lavish, with the people more subdued. There is one exception. The railway station has an illuminated display reproduction of our fleet as it appears in the harbor, incredible. (157)

Most of the houses are only one story. They tell me it's because the women don't want to climb stairs. The streets are too wide to have the arches as we saw in Sydney, so they mainly have flags here. Sad to say, we have also observed the ever-present Japanese spies who appear to be following our fleet.

As I have said before, the officers are not as fortunate as I am. Saturday evening they had to attend a dinner given by the President at Queen's Hall. Portraits of all of our presidents hang in the hall alongside portraits of King Edward and Queen Alexandra. That night began, once again, the full schedule

of speech giving. Not only do the captains and admirals have to attend all the daily functions, but each occasion requires a different uniform.

Every day a launch from the Melbourne newspaper, *The Age*, comes alongside each vessel delivering a huge mailbag full of letters from the new girlfriends acquired in Sydney. But you know there is only one letter I am longing to receive, and only one dear girl I am longing to hear from.

Melbourne declared a holiday on Monday for our parade, even closing the cemeteries. As I mentioned, the excursion from our ship to the city was a long one, but that day we also had to march an exhausting five miles after that. All along the parade route, I saw banners hung with "Big Brother" imprinted, the title of a song that had been composed for our benefit. Wherever we went for the next few days, we heard that song played along with our own National Anthem.

There were so many people gathered for the parade, we became concerned about the control of so boisterous a crowd. When we finally arrived at the parade route, we found temporary fences about four feet high, erected all along the streets to keep our route clear. It made it easier, as if anything could, to march through the miles of cheering people. Only three bands had to play in the parade; luckily, I was not among them. (The musical piece continually played by our bands is

Admiral Sperry attended seventeen dinners, dances, and parties in one day. Only the wives were going strong through the entire stay. It became difficult for Sperry to give speeches throughout Australia and never say what the Australians longed to hear, that the Americans were taking their side against Asia.

The Naval Parade of American Sailors at Melbourne, Australia. August 31, 1908.

7

President Roosevelt took part in the court-martial that followed this incident. The offending seaman was ejected from the service, and the others were severely punished.

one I have heard you play in Kentucky Min, "Honey Boy." It brings back a lot of memories.)

But the parade did not go as planned. The morning started out with fine weather, but as we stepped onto the pier, the clouds came in accompanied by strong gale winds. It didn't take long before my uniform was covered in dust and my eyes and nose to be all gritty; another reason I was grateful not to be blowing my horn. We had to plod mile after mile in the face of that driving dust, I was half choked, and my feet became quite sore. (158)

At the head of the *Louisiana's* detachment, a midshipman stumbled over trolley tracks, swerved and went from one side of the street to the other. Unfortunately, the companies that followed him did the same thing. What a disaster! One seaman collided with another. Others wandered from the parade, and I don't think they ever returned. There will certainly be a high price to pay for that blunder! By the time we reached the heart of the city, I'm sure we looked quite dirty and weary. The parade had lost its usual polish. (159) We all agreed, we've had to march in too many parades.

After the parade, we were each presented with a bouquet of Australia's national flower, the wattle blossom. We were then free to go to the theaters or back to the ship. There was a formal banquet for the officers after the parade at the Parliament House, but there were so many people and the streets so crowded that some of the officers couldn't get near the House to attend their dinner!

On Tuesday, myself and 300 other men and officers went on a special excursion

HANDS ACROSS THE SEA

Leo

Joey

8

train to visit the city of Ballarat, which is about 100 miles inland. The city is where the world's largest gold fields are located. People all along the way waved and cheered as we rode past. Geelong, a small town about halfway, furnished us with boxed lunches and postcards as you can see, as well as souvenir pamphlets. The only drawback—we had to march through the city of Ballarat in a downpour of rain to where they were serving a large banquet.

While I was on shore leave, about 500 school children visited our ship. (It is always easier showing children around the ship than their parents, but I was glad to have missed it for a day out.)

When I returned to the ship the Salvation Army, came aboard and gave us a musical concert. They have a very good band Min, it was relaxing and easy to listen. Wednesday morning I just wandered around the city, it was so calm and peaceful and so inviting to spend time in their beautiful parks. I wish you could have been here to enjoy them with me. But never mind, another time. I spent the afternoon watching a baseball game with our team playing East Melbourne.

With loving thoughts from Your Boy,

Maurice

ON THE MARCH FROM PORT MELBOURNE TO THE CITY OF MELBOURNE
AUG. 31, 1908.

12

5 September

Dearest,

Yesterday was our last day here, and what a day. It was also Admiral Sperry's 61st, birthday, so Melbourne declared a full holiday with celebrations all over the city. We had a spectacular review at Flemington Racecourse (160), after another five to six mile march from the dock! (Maybe after reading all these letters you will have some sympathy for my poor feet and understand why I don't care for parades.) Even though the ground was dry, there were a lot of mud pools we constantly had to wade through because it had rained the day before. I was among some15,000 troops that took part in this review. A train took us back to Williamstown afterward to be rid of our leggings and rifles so we could enjoy a badly needed luncheon.

The celebrations were to end last night with a prepared dinner set for 3,000 men. We all received invitations to the 7:00 o'clock affair. A total of one sailor arrived on time. I must add that I politely declined the invitation ahead of time. I knew I didn't want to spend time sitting in a hall having dinner on my last night here. These gracious people seeing only one man had arrived, postponed the event until 9:00pm. By the time the clock struck 9:00, there were only seven sailors in the hall. What an embarrassment for the fleet as a whole! But it was also a demonstration of how we all felt about Melbourne; We felt it was the best port of call for the entire cruise thus far, and didn't want to waste a moment experiencing the people and life of the city. (161) The only drawback were the elevated prices; nearly doubled I was told.

This evening ended with another fantastic show of fireworks. Many Bluejackets watched the light show with one or two girls on each arm, but always remember, there is only one girl for me. (If you were here today I would kiss you impulsive.) By the time our liberty ended, and everyone started to head back to the train station, the girls hugged and kissed the sailors, ripping off the buttons from their tunics as well as the ribbons from their caps. Because of the crowds, it was hard to reach the train station. Many of the men were physically lifted up shoulder high and carried along the route to board the train on time.

Dearest, I am sorry to report the *Connecticut* had a tragedy on their ship. You are always asking about our pets, well one of their kangaroos met its death on Sunday night. Sunday evening several of the sailors were feeding the kangaroos, and the black bear was not happy with the attention they were receiving. The bear has been aboard longer, so considered himself the main mascot for the sailors. Standing by and watching the kangaroos receiving the attention he was used to, he suddenly attacked one of the new arrivals. The fight was hopeless, I'm sorry to say. The sailors did all they could to drag the animals apart, but the bear made it a fight to the finish. The men of the *Connecticut* mourn their loss deeply. (162) It would have been very shocking to watch.

A kangaroo on yet another ship also lost his life. This story is even sadder. The animal was so thrilled when given freedom from its close confinement under hatches that it began high vaulting on deck and struck its head with full force against a heavy iron pipe. At least I am told, on board the *Vermont* the bear and the kangaroo are getting along, and seem to be great friends.

The *Ohio* also reported they had lost their bear and so requested a *joey* to take its place. But it seems their bear cub had only been lying low; we all hope the same fate that struck those other two kangaroos will not occur on the *Ohio*.

Welcome to Our
American Comrades

Added to this we had two more disasters in this city. A 24-year-old seaman from the *New Jersey* was run over by a Melbourne train and died today. A musician from the *Vermont*, who had been with the Navy for some time, was also run over by a train. The paper said he died from shock due to his injuries. (163) If you ask me, there are just too many people crowded into such a small city.

We upped anchor this morning and I am exhausted! But before we left, the *Vermont* was presented with two collies to add to their growing number of animals. The *Nebraska* received a wombat and another monkey and the *Georgia* received a Kookaburra— a laughing kingfisher that laughs at the smallest gesture.

These animals added to the ships' already menagerie.
All these animals roamed the decks freely, creating a number of hazards. (164)

We left the *Kansas* behind to pick up our mail, which is to arrive in Melbourne in a couple of days. I am so hopeful that when we see the *Kansas* again, there will be an answer from you. I am almost afraid to hear from you again. Honestly, I am; please allay my fears. The photo Frank shot of you in Los Angeles is my only companion. It is so sweet and good to look at. In reviewing your thoughts, please let them dwell on a lonely fellow far away.

Faithfully Yours,

Maurice

300 men failed to report to duty having decided to make Melbourne their home. There were thirty deserters in Sydney and several dozen in Auckland. Added to the deserters in Melbourne, that represented almost a full ship's complement. With the royal treatment they received, it is not surprising the men wanted to stay. "So enthusiastic was the welcome of our fleet that the word, 'fleetitis' was coined to express the fever of hospitality which swept over Sydney and Melbourne." (165)

The fifteen battleships left Melbourne the same way they had arrived: one of the ships plowed into the British steamer, the *Laura*. Melbourne was also left with many people in the hospital, having been trampled or fallen off buildings while watching the parades. A grandstand had collapsed, a bridge had broken from the weight of the crowds, and an out of control trolley killed two sailors. Those two men had to wait to be buried; Melbourne wanted nothing as dismal as a funeral to mar the celebrations. The *Kansas* stayed behind not only to pick up the mail but to represent the fleet in court, pay damages and take back some of the stragglers. When she left Melbourne on 10 September, she was carrying 458 bags of mail and had retrieved a hundred sailors.

"AMERICA'S MIGHT."
Fac-simile reproduction of large picture worked in Silk on the **Light Running "NEW HOME" Sewing Machine** (at our Show Rooms, **746 George Street, Haymarket**), as a Souvenir of the Visit of the United States of America Fleet.
Sydney—August, 1908.   J. W. JOHNSTON & CO.

The seas south of Australia had been given the name "the world's greatest roller-coaster." For six days and 1,300 miles, the fleet traveled up and down the swells suffering from fatigue and seasickness.

17 September 1908

Dear Girl,

Your long letter arrived at last. We haven't received any mail since we were out to sea from Hawai'i! Your letter raised my poor spirits as only your letters can. It was so good to hear that you are well.

I've been feeling very poorly the last few days; awful bad cold. My joints ache fearfully. I am doping up on Quinine in the hope of breaking up the cold. Dear one, I feel oh so lonely when I am not well. I will be glad to be homeward bound. The good old U.S.A. for mine. I'm writing Frank today as well after reading with joy your sweet answer to my question. I am imploring him for the right to take your hand in marriage, and I'll anxiously await his answer. I am sure he will agree; you are the one for me.

The main reason we have stopped in Albany is to coal before the long run of 3,500 miles to Manila. We have just finished.

Even though this area is the largest territory in Western Australia, it has the smallest population. I'm told there are only about 4,000 people who live in Albany. This stop couldn't have happened at a better time—everyone is exhausted. We needed a place to recuperate after all the entertainment in New Zealand and Australia, and the rough seas we encountered from Melbourne to Albany. That doesn't mean Albany has been total relaxation. There were still activities planned for us. Boat races and football games, and of course we had to march in another parade in rainy weather under decorated arches of welcome. That's probably why I feel so poorly. We also illuminated our ships each evening we were in port for the people on shore. Perth, a city about 400 miles from Albany, sent two tons of sausages a day to Albany for 'Fleet Week.' They were mighty tasty. The Australians all along the route have gone to great lengths to entertain us.

There was no musical band in Albany, so at each formal party the Prime Minister of Western Australia played the "Star Spangled Banner" on a piano. They needed you and Frank to create some *good* music.

There is always the feeling, as well as statements in the newspapers, throughout Australia that she wants more Americans to immigrate to their country. That is probably why we had such a tremendous welcome wherever we went. (166)

More animals have come aboard our ships. Our fleet received six emus, which are similar to the ostrich, two more kangaroos, and eight more parrots. It is proving to be a very interesting group of animals sailing together. Our ship resembles a floating zoo . . . and it's beginning to smell like one too!

The emu is about 25% shorter than the ostrich and has three toes; The ostrich has only two (the only bird with two toes). Both belong to the same order of birds but not the same family.

I'm sorry this is such a short letter. I am anxious to get this and Frank's letter in the mail before we leave for Manila. I so long to be with you again. Won't this time ever pass?

Admiral Sperry had his hands full. There had been a lack of communication, and the colliers did not fulfill their contract. When the fleet arrived in Albany, there were only three colliers instead of the needed six, making each ship 500 tons short. The Admiral spent his time negotiating for Australian coal, which unfortunately burned too quickly and fell through the grate bars. It was easy to see the control England could have over the American Navy half a world away from home.

On 18 September 5:00 pm, fifteen battleships left Albany displaying spectacular maneuvers to the Australians on shore; the *Connecticut* was still in the process of refueling. It would take several months after the visit for Australia to realize how mislead she had been in assuming the fleet's purpose. In late 1908, England released Australia from the binding clause in the Anglo-Japanese alliance and agree to the creation of a separate navy.]

MANILA

Singalong Garden, Manila P. I.

The primary concern during this run was the consumption of coal by two ships in the Fourth Division. Sperry ordered the *Kentucky* and the *Kearsarge* to reduce their speed to nine knots. The rest of the fleet cruised at eleven knots leaving the two ships behind. They reunited on 30 September forming a single file into the Basilan Strait. The equator was crossed for the fourth time on 1 October and 2 October. The fleet reassembled into two columns, dropping anchor two miles off the shore of Manila.

6 October 1908

Dear Girl,

When we arrived here in Manila on 2 October, there were no citizens or receptions to greet us. All the celebrations had been canceled due to an outbreak of cholera. They had, however, erected arches, put up decorations, and prepared elaborate celebrations—perhaps in hopes to not to reveal their health problem to the fleet. As far as they were concerned, the disease has diminished, and the drinking water

2

U. S. BATTLESHIP WISCONSIN, LENGTH 373 FT. 10¼ IN.,
BREADTH 72 FT. 2½ IN., DRAFT 23 FT. 8⅓ IN.,
PLACE LAUNCHED SAN FRANCISCO, CAL.

in public places is no longer contaminated as all the filth has been cleaned up. (167) We've heard around 13,000 people died of Cholera in the past five months. I guess there just wasn't enough money to deal adequately with the disease, yet the papers said the citizens raised $120,000 for our entertainment! That is twice what Sydney spent. The only way any of us will go to shore is if we're directed to go on an errand for one of the commanding officers.

The people of Manila are very upset that we are staying aboard our ships when they believe all is safe. It was finally agreed we would return after our visit to Japan. Manila could save the money collected until that time.

Our main reason for stopping here is to re-coal and to get underway as quickly as possible, so you'll have to wait for your postals of this area.

If you could possess my feelings today, you would know my heart aches for you. How my heart longs for you and without you, it will perish.

With a heart full of passion for you alone,

Maurice

Sperry continued to have misgivings about Japan. He was aware as Japan was hanging banners and flags the entire Imperial Navy was at sea and ready for battle. Sperry once again voiced his concern about the color white for the battleships. His ships could be spotted six miles away while it was a mile and a half before the darker painted ships could be seen.

Issued by the Department of Communications in commemoration of the Visit of the American Fleet, Oct. 1908.

19 October 1908

Dearest Girl,

After the longest voyage in history, we finally arrived in Japan yesterday. No doubt you have read in your local paper of the typhoon that struck us and carried our boats away. Minnie, I can't begin to describe it to you. Just look at mountains, like the ones Frank and I explored outside of Frisco, and compare them to the seas that we were in. According to the weather station in Manila, this storm was the worst since 1867. I now know what a rough sea is like!

We left Manila on Friday, 9 October with calm weather. Sunday night, the nearly full moon shined brightly

The Virginia taking one over her bow.

Copr. 1904. Brown + Snapper.
The Wisconsin in a Typhoon, China Sea.

Copr. 1904. Brown + Snapper.
The Virginia going into a heavy swell.

above a smooth, calm sea. Before daylight on Monday, orders came down to make everything secure. The wind started to blow at about 25 mph. By breakfast, the winds had reached 38 mph, and by 8:00 pm, they had clocked in at 45 mph. We extended our distance between ships to 800 yards and slowed our speed to 8 knots.

The winds reached over 100 mph, the rain came down in torrents, and the sea became a mountain range. I'm still amazed we survived the storm! The wireless antenna was carried away, which ended all communications. I never felt so alone. Solid walls of water, sometimes rising sixty feet, shattered the bridge windows and ruined navigational charts. Several times the deck rails became submerged as the ship dove into the sea. I went below and saw the firemen bracing themselves against the furnace doors to prevent the burning coals from spilling out. (168) The raging sea splintered lifeboats on the *Wisconsin*, the *New Jersey*, and our ship, the *Virginia*. Of course, no one slept during this storm. We had to maintain a tight grip to keep from falling.

All the upper decks inside the superstructure flooded. Added to all that discomfort, the ventilation in our ship was shut off except in sickbay where it had been left in place on the forward deck. It didn't take long for the ship to become a nauseating steam bath. Even the sickbay was not left in peace. A big wave leaped over the bow, snapped off the ventilator with a roar, and then went down the hole to sickbay to harass the ailing. (169) We had to drop out of the column to do repairs. Sperry told the Fourth Division to go off by itself and try to handle the storm on its own. We didn't see them for five days. The *Kearsarge* lost its foretopmast and was off by itself away from its division for six days. (170) A horrifying time for all.

Early in the storm, the *Rhode Island* lost a gunner's mate overboard. The *Rhode Island* was at the end of the formation and could not come about to rescue the poor fellow. The seas were too high to launch her lifeboats, and there were no ships to pick him up. Around 11:00 am, the *Minnesota* also reported a man overboard. He had been on the quarterdeck securing ventilators when a wave

swept him out to sea. Fortunately, the *Vermont* was able to rescue him. Later, on Monday, word came from the Fourth Division about a man from the *Illinois* who had been swept out to sea. Luckily, he was picked up by the *Kentucky*. All the ships sustained damages. When the wind died down, we rendezvoused for repairs and exhaled a huge sigh of relief.

The poor animals. You remember I told you each ship was given either a kangaroo or a wallaby? Unfortunately, most of these animals just couldn't get used to ship life and have died. I can't remember if I told you about the couple dingoes the fleet received from Australia. A dingo is like a wild dog. The dingo on the *Louisiana* came from the zoo, so it took him a while to get used to roaming freely on his ship. It wasn't long before he learned how to play ball and other games with the men on deck. This dingo developed a habit of going back and forth on the quarterdeck

looking at the water below. Unfortunately, just before the ship steamed into the Java Sea one morning, the *Louisiana* lurched and the poor dingo went overboard. He swam pretty well. No one knew he had gone overboard, and of course couldn't see him. I'm sorry to say, but our ship plowed right into him. Gone was the *Louisiana's* dingo! I tell you this because you asked me to I report all the happenings with the animals.

We are going ashore shortly to attend a garden party in Yokohama Park, so will write a long letter to you later when I can include some postals.

Please let yourself be guided by the purity of your precious heart, and look lovingly into the future and see if you can see happiness there always, lest we drift beyond the lifeline. My heart cries for your happiness always, and may no cloud ever blur your dear loving heart.

Yours forever,

Maurice

Japan had her reasons for wanting a visit from the fleet. Japan wanted the United States to back her for the expansion into Manchuria. To promote American sympathies, the Japanese decided to make their pageant and celebrations bigger and better than China's could ever be. Some people in Washington wanted only part of the fleet to visit Tokyo Bay, but Japan would not hear of it.

The *New York Times* reported on 20 August 1908, the hatred for America had reached an all-time high in Tokyo, and the Japanese Government was considering canceling the pageant.

The Pacific Fleet of eight cruisers then towed torpedo boats to Samoa to have more fighting force near Japan as a precautionary measure. There was also the promise of support from the Germans if war broke out. As the cruisers and torpedo boats landed in Samoa, they had orders to quickly return home leaving the Atlantic Fleet unprotected.

20 October 1908

Dearest,

I so look forward to my free time, as I can't wait to answer your delightful letter and share the details of our cruise.

Because of the storm, I mentioned in my last letter, we arrived in Tokyo Bay Sunday, 19 October—24 hours later than scheduled. Even though it was somewhat foggy, I could see Fujiyama in the distance with glittering snow, a great postcard, don't you think?

There was a lot of tension on board as we approached the bay. We had no idea what to expect when we saw the Japanese fleet come out of Yokohama. All our guns were ready, and the ammunition was up from the magazines. Then we held our breath—nothing, thank goodness. The only shooting in Tokyo Bay that day was the national salute being fired to each other's flags. (171)

As we entered the bay in column formation, six large steamers loaded with sightseers carrying welcome signs greeted us singing our American songs in their learned English. Along with the steamers was a *Fairy Boat* hired by the American wives. The wives and daughters of the officers had arrived several weeks earlier on their steamer, they were fortunate to have missed the typhoon.

You should have seen the bay. Numerous boats sailed around us from every direction, passing and re-passing us, waving and shouting

with their bands playing the "Star Spangled Banner." As we dropped anchor, sixteen Japanese warships slipped between us giving each of our battleships with a *mate ship*. As soon as we arrived in port, the fireworks began and sirens shrieked. When we looked away from the city of Yokohama, we saw thousands of people lining every vantage point.

Today was declared American Day in Tokyo. (Tokyo is about eighteen miles from Yokohama.) The Japanese housed the four admirals and captains in first class hotels in Tokyo, where they'll remain as guests of the Emperor until Friday.

To begin the festivities, a garden party was held in Shinjuku Imperial Gardens for the officers. Arrangements were made for 2,400 men to go ashore for a garden party at Hibiya Park, Tokyo. Before we could go ashore we were told President Roosevelt had given orders that only the special first class men would be allowed to go ashore; men that could be counted on to behave. We received orders detailing our responsibilities representing America.

Roosevelt's main concern when he accepted the Japanese invitation had been misbehavior on the part of enlisted men ashore, and he wanted to issue the order that no enlisted man be given liberty while in Yokohama. Sperry strongly advised Roosevelt against any *obvious departure* from normal practice. (172)

We were then put into groups of fifty, each commanded by an officer. We were told that even though this was entertainment, it was also a matter of duty (173) and were warned that if anyone does anything to attract negative attention, it will result in a general court martial. (174) I sure remember those words!

There were three piers specially constructed for us in Yokohama decorated with greens and flowing draperies. We all received a medal with an anchor and crossed flags of the two countries which we were instructed by our commanders to wear every time we went ashore. I'll save it for you as a souvenir.

We were escorted by Japanese guides and marched as a group to the railway station. At the station, a tea garden was set up for us. Yokohama's fair ladies in their gorgeous kimonos served delicious tea in fragile cups and 'Welcome' cakes on decorative trays. (175)

This was amazing, Minnie. Let me try to take you there in words:

When we reached Tokyo, other musical bands from our fleet joined us, and we marched to Hibiya Park. The route was lined with so many people. At the entrance to the park was a huge arch decorated with greenery and flowers. Fireworks exploded all around us until late into the night.

Once in the park, we saw twenty-five entertainment platforms set up offering theaters, refreshment booths, bandstands, wrestling matches, and tea gardens which we all enjoyed. Adjoining

the park were long banquet tables loaded with food. At the center of the arena was a large stage that became the focus of the activities—the Geisha dance. The dancers formed the words: "Welcome, Hail Columbia" through graceful movements. (176) It was uniquely mesmerizing. After the performance, we heard the command of 'squads right!' (177) Thus, began our march back to the station, a very full day.

When we returned to our ships, we displayed our usual illuminations and fireworks.

(Y.174)　　Custom House Yokohama.　　　横浜税関

Yokohama

26 October

Dearest,

Yesterday morning we upped anchor at 8:30 am and departed Yokohama. Each ship made a quick turn out to sea while our bands played Japan's anthem. A Japanese warship accompanied each of our battleships; they will leave us later on today. I now have some time to tell you more about our stay in Japan. There were many excursions every day, some I was privileged to attend. There were dinners, receptions, theater parties, garden parties, dances, and more entertainment than I could possibly tell you about. In Yokohama alone, there were parties hosted each day for 1,000 men. Sleep was not written into our schedules.

When I went ashore on Tuesday, it was evident the Japanese spies who had been following us throughout this cruise must have reported home all the details of our previous receptions and pageants. The people had obviously prepared for months for this event. I even heard, the police went around to every household instructing them how many flags and lanterns they had to hang outside their homes, as well as the size, and the materials they had to use. (178)

MY KINGDOM FOR A GEISHA GIRL.

The authorities further demanded that next to every Japanese flag, there had to be an American flag. Walking down the street, I could see that each of these flags were the same material and same size; if the American flag was made of silk, then the Japanese flag was also silk. Every house had a lantern made especially for the fleet's visit with the two flags crossing like the medal we received yesterday. A few men, however, are expressing bitterness over the Japanese government's dictated welcome, calling it a fraud.

The Emperor issued orders for his people during our visiting. I thought you might be interested in a few of these demands I have turned up thanks to an interpreter. Share these with Frank, I'm sure he will enjoy them.

The lowest price for this complete and mandatory decoration was 55 cents that represented two days wages for the laboring man in Japan.

1. Dogs will not have sticks or stones thrown at them nor at the dogs brought ashore by the foreigners.
2. No comments or ridicule of the dress the Americans wear.
3. No staring at the foreigner except when necessary.
4. No spitting and no scattering the skin of fruits or cigarettes ends on a train or on their ship.
5. No finger can be pointed at him.
6. Seat the lady first in a room.

7. Clearing teeth and nostrils when in the presence of a foreigner must use a handkerchief and not fingers.

8. Those learning English cannot try out their language on the foreigners for the sole purpose of practicing.

The Japanese American Embassy is flying the wrong American flag! It has only 45 stars. The rest of Japan obviously researched how many stars are on our flag, because they're all flying the correct version!

I was delighted to see rickshaws and carriages waiting for us each day on the pier. The rickshaw soon became my choice of travel. There are also electric streetcars in Japan that cost only 10 cents to ride for an hour, but they're too crowded for me.

Everyone was very polite and always smiling broadly— good and generous to a fault. I just didn't feel I could trust them. Yet, everywhere we went, the Japanese ran out of their homes to greet us. I was continually having flowers tossed from windows or from a passerby into my rickshaw or having flags thrown at my head. Whenever I stopped, small gifts quickly dropped into my hands and everywhere, I could see groups of children singing "Hail Columbia." (We did not hear our National Anthem sung. As one of the interpreters told me, our national anthem is just too difficult for the Japanese to sing.)

The roads were decorated with bands of red and white, and artificial cherry and apple blossoms. There were arches of ferns built at every important street junction. All along the way, we saw children waving flags, holding bouquets of flowers, and saying in their practiced English "We are glad to see you." (179) The children even created individual postcards at school to commemorate our visit. I wish we could have been here in April to see the Cherry Blossom Festival everyone talks about. It must be beautiful with all the trees in full bloom. Aren't these postals lovely?

I was able to go with a group of men to Yokohama Park where parties were hosted every day for 1,000 men. At the entrance was a huge welcome arch covered in greens and flowers and outlined with electric globes. The park was similar to Hibiya Park in that there were separate areas set up for refreshments, tea gardens, theaters, and banquet tables loaded with food. There was every possible device to make our visit pleasant. (180) Juggling and singing was everywhere. Even the cakes and candies the ladies served in the tea garden were stamped with "Welcome."

The Japanese became concerned we were behaving a little too well, so we must not be having very much fun. To create yet more 'fun,' the entertainment committee filled hundreds of barrels with beer and recruited hundreds of geishas for our pleasure. Well, as you might have guessed, this entertainment did not last long. All were quickly canceled by our superiors. The Navy explained to the Japanese that most of us belonged to the YMCA, and the entertainment we were used to was ice cream socials. The missionaries were also concerned and felt the enlisted men needed protection from the Geisha! After that afternoon, ice cream was served at every function we attended. There was only one sailor I knew who had a problem with this. He was a man from the *Kentucky* who drank lemon extract to become intoxicated because alcohol was strictly forbidden. Unfortunately, he drank too much and received a proper military burial.

Gate made to welcome the American Fleet, Tokio, Japan.

Welcome Decorations for American Fleet.

The Germans sent invitations to the American officers and other American civilians to lure them to their functions while in Japan, but there were no takers. The Japanese newspapers spoke favorably of the pageant, seeing the American fleet as a messenger of peace. There were great sighs of relief all over the world. The four journalists each received gifts of "a little paper house, a silk kimono, and a beautiful maiden. The girls came complete with packets of papers showing that they were legally married to the writers for the duration of the visit." (181) Franklin Matthews reported to the *Sun* that the fleet had fallen in love with Japan and were being followed about by adoring young women.

Another excursion I was able to attend was a trip to Kamakura, a quaint seaside village with old structures. The most popular attraction was the Temple of Hachiman containing the colossal bronze Buddha and the great image of the Goddess Kwannon. Then we went by trolley car to the Buddhist Temple of Kwannon where a luncheon was served with chopsticks! Needless to say, I failed at this task and finally had to use my fingers or I would have gone without!

From there we went on to see the Great Buddha. I was able to obtain postals of all of these sights for you. I learned many interesting things that day, but I remember a couple in particular. When parents name a new child, they take him to the nearest temple. They write different names for the baby on separate sheets of paper and give them to the priest who throws them in the air and asks the gods to direct the lot. The first piece of paper that touches the ground becomes the child's name. And how about this? In every temple we visited, I saw pilgrims write requests on paper, chew them up and then spit them toward the mouth to the idol. If it sticks, their prayer will be answered. (182) I saw several idols covered with small bits of paper.

To enter a building in Japan, everyone has to take off his shoes. I must confess this was a problem because few of us had the time to mend the holes in our socks before we landed. The Japanese weren't offended, though. They just devised a cover to put over our shoes so we would not be embarrassed.

Some of the officers returning to the ship told us young Geisha girls sat on their laps while they ate at restaurants, offering them saké, and asking to be taken to America!

Thursday was yet another marching parade with entertainment following.

Friday evening, Admiral Toga gave a dinner on the battleship *Fuji* for the American officers and their wives. Following the dinner was a ball and reception aboard Admiral Toga's old flagship, the *Mikasa*. Rumors certainly spread quickly at the end of that evening.

It is said there was a beautiful waterfall and a movie show for entertainment on the quarterdeck. I was told the Americans were able to contain their drinking of expensive wines and fine champagnes, but the Japanese could not. When Admiral Sperry said goodnight, the Japanese put the Admiral on a blanket and tossed him up in the air three times and then paraded him around the decks! They repeated this with the other Commanders. What a sight that must have been! Too bad Frank couldn't be there with his camera!

Grand Hotel at Yokohama.

The *Connecticut* reciprocated by giving a party on Saturday. Congress had given the fleet additional money after Peru ($75,000 (183) or $7,500 (184)), but by the time we reached Japan, it was depleted so there was very little money to spend for the occasion. This proved to be an embarrassment to the United States. Several thousand guests were invited and hundreds more made their way on board. Many of the people arrived early in the morning so by the time the reception actually began, the refreshments were gone. A conference was held midday, and the officers decided to chip in their personal earnings. Boats were sent for more candy, sandwiches, wines, and cigars. With all the visitors, this new supply only lasted until late afternoon. When Admiral Togo, the Imperial Princes, the Prime Minister, and other

Admiral Sperry and Sailors witnessing a Geisha performance. Yokohama, Japan

A Sampan is a small East Asia boat, typically with an oar or oars at the stern.

notables came aboard, there was nothing left of the refreshments. The contrast between the lavish affair given by the Japanese and the shabby affair hosted by the Americans was noted in the Japanese newspapers the following day.

On our last night in Yokohama, the Japanese celebrated with an enormous torchlight parade. Mile after mile of cheering people marched carrying colorful a lanterns on the end of sticks painted with crossed Japanese and American flags. Admiral Sperry was given a special stand so he could see this extraordinary scene. "The Star Spangled Banner" was played continuously by different Japanese bands. At the same time, hundreds of lantern-carrying sampans formed a long line behind the breakwater and then wound in and out of our ships. It resembled a glowing sea serpent dancing all around us. (185)

Towards the end of the evening, the cornet brigade played "Auld Lang Syne" and "Home Sweet Home," which only reminded me of the oceans that span our separation. How long seems the time ere I can claim you as my own sweet darling wife? Dear one, I suffer for the want of your pure sweet love and care, but I know I must wait just a few more months. If I were only there with you—well, you know the result, for I would be perfectly wild!

The parade was originally to contain 15,000 people but grew to well over 50,000! Admiral Sperry and the other admirals viewed this extraordinary scene from a special stand for an hour - -while massed bands played 'Star Spangled Banner' continuously." (186)

I have been down and out for the past two days. My teeth are very troublesome, and I long to be home and have them fixed properly. I am sending you my picture on a rickshaw, it is on its way soon if nothing happens. I have also sent some cards to Frank.

I will write again from China when I have some time. Again, remember sweet girl, your letters mean so much to me. I long to hear from you soon.

Your faithful heart until the grave,

Maurice

Sperry was not originally going to take on coal in Yokohama even though the American Navy had maintained a small coal depot there; the social calendar was too strenuous. However, because of the typhoon and its unexpected toll on fuel consumption, about "3,500 tons of coal were slowly loaded into barges and, as the fleet enjoyed Japanese hospitality, were conveyed to the ships and stowed in their bunkers." (187)

The shopkeepers and rickshaw people were, by government order, not to raise their prices. The Japanese officials called upon all of Tokyo's publishers telling them anyone who failed to publish the proper enthusiasm for the fleet would be taxed out of business or heavily fined. Japan gave the Americans everything they wanted. According to many of the references, Japan— out of fear— backed down and changed her aggressive mind after viewing Roosevelt's demonstration of power, the Atlantic Fleet. But even though words of friendship were exchanged during the fleet's visit, other countries were preparing and making plans for a Pacific conflict. "Roosevelt later wrote that the reception in Japan was 'the most noteworthy incident of the cruise.' " (188)

CHINA

Marines taking a Rickashaw Ride at Chefoo, China.

In 1908, the 264-year-old empire, located in the Forbidden City, was crumbling. Chaos was everywhere. Nations wanted to expand their control in China and increase their grant leases on her coast. The biggest pressure was coming from Japan to strengthen its hold on China in Southern Manchuria.

China was aware of the effect the fleet pageants were having on Japan. She did all she could to spread rumors of impending attacks on the American fleet by Japan. (189) The proposed visit from the fleet gave hope to the Chinese. Rumors in China stated America was going to put an end to Japanese operations in Manchuria. Germany held the same hope, and wanted the United States to establish a naval base on the "Shantung peninsula, from which the Americans could help Germany prevent the 'partition' of China by the Japanese, British, French, and Russians." (190) China began designing a giant demonstration against Japan by preparing for the visit of the fleet. The Chinese expected their grand pageant to symbolize the new alliance with America that would save their country from the internal and external forces that threatened her.

After much debate between the White House and the Department of the Navy, Shanghai was chosen for the pageant. Thousands of workers were sent to Shanghai to work on decorations to welcome the fleet. The Department of the Navy ended up rejecting Shanghai because of dangerous currents. The White House and China's Ambassador worked toward another solution to the problem and decided on Chefoo as the port of choice. The workers were then moved to Chefoo to erect special landing piers and pink pavilions with baby blue arches for the parades.

After further consideration, the Department of the Navy once again stepped in and said Chefoo would add 2,000 miles and 8,000 tons of coal to their itinerary, thus delaying target practice in Manila. Plans were changed again. It was then decided the first and Second Division would steam to Chefoo while the second squadron would go to Manila for target practice. After all, the fleet was also on a target practice cruise. China was beside herself and riots broke out. The entire fleet visited Tokyo, why not China? By this time, the Department of the Navy wanted to cancel the visit to China altogether.

More debates in Washington and the destination was moved once again to Amoy, a port of no importance to China. The workers were moved south to Amoy to build another pleasure city for the fleet. With these changes, China had to raise more money to complete the new structures. China was beginning to lose face.

The first week in October, 600 servants arrived in Amoy with food, drink, horses, carriages, and rickshaws to await the guests. However, the same typhoon the fleet battled in route to Japan came ashore in Amoy, killing about 3,000 people, flattening the pleasure city, and leaving the parade grounds in three feet of water. The government replenished the budget, increasing the cost of the pageant to $1,000,000— about seven times the money spent by any other country. (191) The workers worked around the clock for ten days to repair the damage. As the American fleet neared China, a rumor circulated about a plot to kill one of the Chinese officials during the visit. An extra 2,000 policemen were sent from the neighboring cities, and 5,000 soldiers arrived from the Forbidden City for security. " . . . guards were placed every ten feet along the route from the fleet landing to the entertainment ground, where an additional one hundred men guarded each entrance, and no Chinese were admitted without passes." (192)

Admiral Sperry and the first squadron sailed past Amoy to the Philippines leaving the third and Fourth Divisions to visit China. This created another

Xiamen, formerly Amoy, is a sub-provincial city in southeastern Fujian, China insult aimed at China. The Chinese newspapers tried to save face. They printed stories that the first and Second Divisions were lost at sea during the typhoon, and had not been seen since. China's enthusiasm waned, and further riots broke out as the second squadron approached Amoy.

4 November 1908

Dearest girl,

A mind that is tortured with longings as mine is, can in no way express itself on this unfeeling paper. Though my writing tends to be in the form of a journal, please remember that I am always longing for your dear sweet heart.

We leave China tomorrow, and I couldn't be more grateful. I will be so thankful when we are homeward bound. The only way I could tell a man from a woman in this country is by their hair. The men shave a part of their head.

We arrived in China on Friday morning, 30 October, but were only greeted by a Chinese gunboat and a German gunboat. The Germans were everywhere trying to assume a role in the pageant. Arriving, we heard another rumor: we were here to bombard Amoy and use it as a base of operations against Japan. We could see thousands of frightened people leaving the city of Amoy carrying their possessions on their backs and dragging their carts to get away from our approaching ships.

It wasn't until Sunday that we received word the area was secure enough for liberty, and then we were not allowed into the city of Amoy. Instead, we were ferried to a newly constructed pier and then to an entertainment center called the Pleasure City.

In this Pleasure City, there were six pavilions containing bamboo screens with crepe paper pasted inside. Each building could seat about

The Entertainment of the Officers of the American Fleet in Amoy.

3

Unfortunately one of the pavilions caught fire and it was not long before the entire Pleasure City collapsed, destroying approximately ten thousand post cards.

Approximately 15,000 cigars and 60,000 cigarettes were given to the men.

500 men. On the one side of the pavilions were lacquered eagles and dragons. There were nine entertainment halls set in an oval pattern enclosing a football field and a baseball diamond! At one end of the oval was a large arch carved and inlaid with nautical designs. At the other end was the Officers' Pavilion with heavy brocaded silk ceilings. Walking past this area, I saw the fancy decorations set up for the officers: jade statues, silver bowls, lacquered vases, furniture that looked to be made of ebony with mother-of-pearl, and satin wall hangings, just to name a few. (193) This had to have been quite a project to construct. There was even an electric lighting station and a small railroad to haul the building supplies, two large Chinese theaters, and a YMCA pavilion where free cigars and cigarettes were handed out.

I spent most of my time at the YMCA pavilion. That's where I bought some cards for you and Frank. We were fed every day with the food brought in from Shanghai. Try to picture this, the Chinese also built a shelter for all the servants, because the cooks and servers came from Shanghai and Peking, the actors came from Canton, and the policemen were from Amoy to keep everything secure.

At first, free beer and soft drinks were given out to us, but it only took a couple of days before orders came down that beer could only be served with our meals. The officers were served the finest European wines during their meals. And the meals! Two days we were served Chinese food, the next two days we ate excellent European food.

There were football and baseball games every day, and I must tell you our boys from the *Virginia* won the football finals against the *Louisiana*. Our ship received a large gold cup valued at $1,200, and each of us on the team received a miniature gold cup which I will save for you.

This afternoon, the last day of our visit, the Chinese gave us some very expensive gifts. Each ship received a beautiful silver bowl. The Admirals and Captains received a large silver bowl, two chairs, and a table inlaid with ebony. The commanding officers received dressing sets and ivory jewel boxes, and the men all received a cloisonné cup. The entertainment tonight is to be a large fireworks display hosted by the Chinese.

Do not judge our life in the Navy as a holiday, Minnie, because of my descriptions of our time ashore. Work dominates the Navy, and if there is any slack time, you can be sure that work will be found for us to do! That's why it is so difficult to write as often as I would like. Time is slipping quite fast, but it just can't go fast enough for me. The light of my life will ever shine as the sun and no cloud can darken it, and you sweet darling, are my light.

Maurice

At 8:00 am, 5 November 1908, honors and salutes were exchanged and the second squadron upped anchor for Manila. The *Louisiana* took Admiral Emory to Hong Kong, as his retirement date coincided with the departure from Amoy. Once the squadron was outside the harbor, a salute was fired for the retiring Admiral.

Manila's Welcome Arch in Honor of the visit of the American Fleet.

The entire fleet met in Manila on 9 November for target practice. The death rate from cholera was reported to be slightly higher than it had been during the fleet's first scheduled visit. The ship's doctors went ashore and voted four to three that it was too dangerous to have a pageant in Manila. The city was livid. They accused Admiral Sperry of stealing the $1,500,000 raised for the celebration. The Lt. Governor wired President Roosevelt telling him that without the pageant, the prestige of the government and the fleet would be diminished. Roosevelt ordered the show to begin. Admiral Sperry refused all but one of the invitations, the party at the British consulate. That was one party he had to attend.

20 November 1908

Dear Girl,

Just a few lines today so that my darling heart may know all's well with her boy. I wish I could be with you, how happy I would be. But I mustn't worry about it for I know I have to wait. It does seem so hard to be separated from my ever darling Minnie. Your last letter has caused me more sweet pleasure than any you've written me. How I devoured every precious word knowing of your endearing feelings toward your boy.

We have target practice during the entire month of November, which leaves me little time to visit the city and even less time to write.

This practice is different than the shooting exercise held in Magdalena Bay last March. Magdalena Bay prepared us for Manila Bay. In the spring, it was called record practice to qualify the men to shoot in the battle practice here in Manila. This prepares those men to be ready for real battle. (194) In record practice, each gun, or set of guns, is fired individually with time in between for preparation. In practice, this process goes as fast as possible; we shoot as if the target was actually another warship. This practice goes on all day and half the night. We even pretend to be shot and wounded and are taken to sickbay. There are no prizes given in battle practice as there were in record practice.

When we arrived, the scare of cholera still remained in the city. We were given specific instructions about food and drink before going ashore. If we returned to our ship with any dirt, mud, or filth and/or we were not sober, we landed in isolation for five days. Once again, besides the officers, it was only the special first-class men who were allowed shore leave.

The citizens erected a huge open air hippodrome and staged wild west variety shows. (195) We had guides appointed by the U.S. Army stationed here to show us around. That's how I was able to buy several postals for you and Frank. With the guides, I visited the botanical gardens, which are situated on ten acres of beautiful land. Looking at the post card, it would seem that such scenes of nature would cause us

Street in Pandacan, Manila P. I.

to be more centered in life, don't you think?

I am thankful for the guides because I was able to learn so much more about this country. The main manufacturing interest here is preparing tobacco. Unfortunately, all ages work at the factories from morning until night. We all received boxes of cigars and cigarettes to take back to the ship.

Along the rivers are washerwomen— beating their clothes with flat sticks and rocks. (196) I'm told they bathe, wash their boats, *and* their clothes all in the same water! I think I told you before that the officers take their uniforms ashore at each place we drop anchor and pay for them to be cleaned. With this method of washing the officer's laundry, most of the uniforms came back missing the buttons!

The local beast of burden is called a carabao, which looks like a water buffalo. A black bird, called a martinico, is commonly found on the back of the carabao and accompanies him wherever he goes. The carabao works well with the area's wet rainy season, but on dry hot days, he demands a bath every two hours.

Flying a "homeward-bound pennant."

I don't think we want to live here, L. A. for mine. The houses have only one floor and are supported by poles looking like stilts with thatched roofs. The buzzing skitters all around us look as large as jacksnipes. (197) We don't want to be buried here either. People are buried in rented vaults. If the rent is not paid, eviction takes place!

We leave tomorrow for Colombo, a fourteen day run from here. This begins our homeward bound cruise. I am really feeling the pull towards our homeland now.

Ask Frank to locate the place to join the Musicians Union in California so I can get a card. Darling, you shouldn't worry about our finances for I feel perfectly able to support you and I want you to rest easy on that score. I sometimes think you worry too much about our future. Now I may be a dreamer, but when I dream of our future, I see in my dreams a big strong and healthy man earning his own by hard days of labor and music playing. This is the kind of dream I have.

Hope you are well and happy, my Dear.

Maurice

On 1 December 1908, the fleet sailed from Manila. Each battleship was flying a homeward-bound pennant that was over two hundred feet long.

(right) Photo #: NH 105996 USS Virginia (Battleship #13) taking one over her bow during the fleet's cruise around the World.

Photographed by Brown & Shaffer from on board USS Louisiana (Battleship #19). Collection of Chief Quartermaster John Harold. U.S. Naval History and Heritage Command Photograph.

Collection of photos from the Great White Fleet voyage in 1908. Naval History and Heritage Command, Washington, DC

Sunday, 6 December, the *Connecticut* fired a 21-gun salute as the fleet sailed passed Singapore. Then the drills began again; range finding exercises, signal and maneuver drills. The signal officers worked from 8:00 am to 10:00 or 11:00 pm every night.

The *New Jersey* reported a man overboard on 8 December. The fleet was halted. Searchlights located the man and brought him aboard only to learn there had been two men overboard. The *New Jersey* remained behind for several hours but was unable to locate the missing man.

10 December 1908

Dearest Girl,

I wanted to let my darling heart know all's well with her boy. I have purchased a very unique writing board with various equipment attached that I will send to you as soon as we reach the states. I also bought a nice postal album I think you will enjoy.

Yesterday the doctor on board the *Georgia* diagnosed a case of small pox. The ship was sent directly to Colombo to land the poor man. We all heard about it, and today everyone who had gone ashore in Manila was vaccinated!

The weather has been very good. To help with the boredom en route to Colombo, we had a dance last night. The forecastle was converted into a ballroom. Before the dance, formal invitations were made. "Mr. John Heavy Weather requests the pleasure of your company on Wednesday evening, 9 December 1908 at half-past nine o'clock. Dancing in No.1 Hot Air Lane." Then replies were received, "Mr. & Mrs. Bounding Billow accept with pleasure Mr. John Heavy Weather's kind invitation for 9 December 1908. No. 49 Easy Mark Avenue." (198) Regrets were written and sent back to our hosts from Teddy the bear, Billy the goat, and Charlie the kangaroo. (199) Too bad they were unable to attend the function!

At the appointed hour, we headed to the resort, Hot Air Lane, to be greeted by Heavy Weather on the Gulf and his friends. For the ball be a pleasure for all, there had to be good ventilation. No problem as there was a soothing cool sea breeze, fun arrangements, a solid floor to dance on, and of course, good music. (200) You know there was good music because of the band members, one in particular! Each man chose a partner and danced until the call to arms, which is the bugle call to get your hammocks. Even the band members received a break to take a spin around the floor. All in all, it was a delightful and fun evening of entertainment. But I am sure you can do a much better job of dancing than the partner I chose. I am looking forward to finding out very soon.

I hope you and Frank are doing good with your music. I will send you some nice presents as soon as we're back stateside.

Darling, if I could squeeze you oh so tight just now. Yes, darling, when I come to you, no matter how public the place, I am going right up to you and take you in my arms and hug you good and hard and kiss your dear sweet lips for the first time.

Your Boy,

Maurice

COLOMBO, CEYLON

(right) Collection Photo # UA 493.09.01 Sailors visiting Ceylon (Sri Lanka) during the voyage of the Great White Fleet in 1908.

Collection of photos from the Great White Fleet voyage in 1908. Naval History and Heritage Command, Washington, DC

The world began to see Germany replaced by Great Britain as American's friend. Invitations were written to Roosevelt inviting the fleet to England and to every crown colony that lay anywhere along the fleet's route. Most of these invitations had to be refused. Roosevelt was leaving on a hunting trip March 4, 1909, so the deadline for the return of the fleet to Hampton Roads had to remain as scheduled on February 22, 1909.

18 December 1908

Dearest Minnie,

The light of my life, your dear long looked for letter and cards were waiting here when we arrived. I was so happy to know my Little Girl is well and I am anxiously waiting your next letter.

We dropped anchor in Colombo 13 December after a somewhat uneventful cruise. We drilled most every day, so were kept very busy. We are visiting this country, not because of an invitation, but because of our need to refuel. Sitting in the Indian Ocean, Colombo has seen many a fine ship anchor in her harbor. Almost all ships, when heading home by way of the Suez Canal from the Orient, stop here for coal.

Upon our arrival, all kinds of native merchants came aboard selling their wares. This proved to be quite a problem for our ship's police. The old sea dogs said the traders were trying to sell their goods for about four times their value. They warned all of us that this is a problem at every foreign port. Even a snake charmer came aboard with several cobras coiled around him. You would have loved him! Ha, ha, ha.

2

Colombo did not do much in the way of beautifying their city for us, but they did have a decorated pier and a large triumphal arch with yellow flowers that read "Welcome to the American Fleet." We were greeted by a full entertainment schedule of

Lake Road, Colombo.

receptions, concerts, luncheons, and dinners. Every evening at 2000, our ships were illuminated as we have done in each port, and our bands performed. We usually played lively quickstep melodies and ended the evening with a slow waltz. (201)

Our first morning, a native laundry man approached one of our officers and asked if he had any laundry. I heard the officer reply very loudly that he had none to spare. "We had our laundry scattered all over the world, that which remains is buttonless, and if we lose any more our predicament will be a serious one." (202) He wasn't going to have any of uniforms beat with rocks in the river again!

Bare-skinned native boys are always surrounding our ships, shouting, "Tara-ra-ra-boom-de-ay. You heave, I dive." We throw coins, and the natives dive for them. Almost every dive, the boys retrieve the coins before they reach the bottom. (203) It's a fun game to watch.

I did finally get ashore to locate cards and to see some of the sights. Once again, the transportation of choice was the rickshaw. The people here are the direct descendants of old Egypt, older than any other people. They can trace their civilization back 2,400 years. Why, Alexander the Great visited here!

I was able to tag along on a group tour for a day and was able to learn more about the area and venture further from town.

The dress of the natives is interesting. You wouldn't like it here one bit, Minnie. The women wear rings in their noses and gold embroidered veils over their faces, and you should see the hats! Some are just fancy embroidered cloths, some are flat turbans, and some look like they were made from brass or another type of metal. Even the Europeans have funny hats here which consist of two brims made of felt or a similar material with the lower brim folded around their ears. (204) The children run naked here while the native men wear skirts of purple, green, red, and yellow plaid. Everyone goes barefoot. The group I was touring with ventured into the wrong section of the city by mistake. We wound through areas I'm sure we weren't supposed to see: smelly, crowded streets with very poor housing. I made the mistake of feeling sorry for a begging man who obviously had leprosy. As soon as I gave him a coin, a crowd of lepers followed us for the next two hours. Their pitiful whines still linger in my mind. (205)

Once we were headed back in the right direction, we were taken to many shops, some specializing only in jewelry. A lot of gems are mined and produced here. Some of them are beautiful, but our guide told us that some are only glass. Only the best jeweler can tell them apart. I did not even attempt to bargain with these thieves, though I sure would like to have purchased a pretty gem for my dear sweet girl.

On one street corner, we saw a snake charmer with his assistant beating a drum beside him. Down the way was a musician of sorts

blowing a flute inserted in his nostril. A very nasal sound, not the clear tone of a flute I'm used to. (206) All along the streets, merchants attempted to draw us into their shops to buy merchandise. Almost everyone bought something, if only a small elephant, which is the most common item we saw.

There is a special train set up for us that transports officers and men to the ancient capital of Ceylon some seventy-five miles from Colombo. Quite a few decided to take advantage of this opportunity. Some of us elected to ride on the top of the train cars instead of inside. The train had to stop before entering each tunnel so we could scramble down into the cars. It was great fun. From the top of the train, I saw native villages, tea and rubber plantations, crocodiles, a bear, some wild boar, a cheetah, and some deer while still enjoying the fresh air.

We stopped in Kandy to see the Temple of the Tooth, where a tooth of the Buddha is kept. The heat and humidity here was stifling. I tried to go into a Buddhist temple but I wasn't allowed inside. I never did find out why. We had lunch in Kandy, rode the train back to Colombo, and marched from the train to the jetty to board our ships. All in all, a fascinating day.

Our mascot family has enlarged again. We received two monkeys. Once aboard, Teddy the bear wanted to get acquainted. He rose to an upright position and extended a paw as a form of courtesy. Unfortunately, the monkey didn't appreciate this and made a flying leap up the nearest stay. He climbed up the military mast and took a seat on the signal yard scolding all below. (207)

All the officers received a five-pound box of tea, and each man received a one-pound box. The boxes are made of wood, and printed directly underneath the image of the American and British flags are the words: "Finest hill-grown Ceylon tea, especially selected and packed for presentation to the American Fleet with greetings and good wishes from the Planter's Associations." (208) I will add this box to the presents I'll send when we reach the states.

Duty is waiting for me, so I must once again close my letter. Write as often as you can and send me just a little love. I need it so much. In the treasure of my heart, you hold the most sacred place.

My love to you always,

Maurice

At this point there had been many breakdowns of the ships' steering mechanisms along the route. The hulls and superstructures were repainted numerous times, but nothing could be done about the slime and weeds they dragged along making the vessels very sluggish. The *Kearsarge* seemed to be coming apart, and some of the ships had lost all their lifeboats in storms. Not only were the ships in need of some repair, but the men were getting bored: filled with tension and fatigue. Sailors began settling their differences with fists, were slack in their duties, and complained about the food. Twenty-one sailors were court-martialed from Colombo to Gibraltar because of physical displays of anger and stealing the officers' liquor. On the *Kearsarge*, the captain court-martialed the cook for failing to follow orders and a seaman for stealing a loaf of bread. All shore leave was then canceled for the rest of the cruise after a beefsteak was stolen from the officers' mess. The *Illinois* reported a man overboard on 26 December. He was never recovered.

SUEZ

At the Sphinx, Egypt.

In July 1908, a revolution had taken place in Turkey. The Young Turks had captured the control of the government from the pro-German Sultan (the sovereign of an Islamic Country). Britain came to the support of Turkey. The rest of the world felt that Europe was like "a powder keg ready to explode." (209) As the fleet approached the Suez Canal, an Imperial message reported millions of German troops were ready to be mobilized. England heard many rumors of invasions by sea and air. Parliament demanded six new dreadnoughts to be constructed and issued rifles to the Boy Scouts. (210)

On 28 December 1908, a major earthquake and tidal wave struck the area of Messina, Sicily, completely destroying it. Estimates of between 15,000 to 200,000 people were feared dead. The supply ship *Celtic* loaded with supplies and heading for the fleet was ordered to go to the earthquake zone instead on 31 December.

1 January 1909

My Darling Girl,

This Happy New Year's card comes with a message from my heart to the love of my life. May it ever be mine. How I long to be home and be with the sweet girl of my dreams. I will try and get to shore soon and buy you and Ma's New Year's presents. Let me back up so I can catch you up on the news from aboard ship.

We spent Christmas Day on the Arabian Sea. It was very hot and lonesome here without you. There were no forests to obtain greenery to brighten up the ship this year. The *Louisiana* had a potted palm tree they decorated with painted coconuts and pictures of President Roosevelt. That turned out to be the only holiday greenery in the entire fleet.

Foremost on everyone's mind is getting home. "Merry Christmas" was flashed from ship to ship, and a group of midshipmen serenaded everyone with mandolins, guitars, and ringing bells dressed in kimonos. (211) In the afternoon, we had sack races, three-legged races, potato sack races, and bobbing contests on deck. For the bobbing contest, men had their hands tied behind their backs and ran along the deck to a pail of water full of oranges where he had to dunk his head in the bucket and retrieve an orange. Then he moved onto a bucket of flour containing about eight hidden silver dollars. He had to search through the flour with his teeth looking for the coins. What the men participating didn't know was that under the six-inch layer of flour was a three-inch layer of molasses! (212) Frank and his camera would have been a hit! It was a hilarious.

In the evening, we had our traditional Christmas dinner with turkey, cranberry sauce, and pies. After the meal, our band performed on the upper deck. I found it difficult at times, playing the well-loved Christmas melodies and the few waltzes that were requested. My heart just wasn't in it.

The colors of the sea have been a source of interest for me since the day we left Hampton Roads. We have sailed so many waterways. Sometimes the sea looks to be colorless, at others, a bright blue, and still others ranging from varying shades of green to pure white. In this area of the world, the sea appears red. In this area of the world, the sea appears red. (213) The variety of nature and scenery I have observed have truly delighted me on this tour.

Last night, New Year's Eve, I quite enjoyed the celebration knowing we are that much closer to home and to my darling. At midnight, tins and cans of all sizes were banged. The bells on the ship rang, causing the dogs to howl in chorus. Teddy performed acrobatic stunts (one of the men had taught him), and everyone laughed and cheered. It will be a celebration I won't soon forget.

Tonight, we will have turkey dinner again, and my band will entertain the men with a concert this afternoon and again this evening. We crossed the equator for the sixth time since leaving Hampton Roads.

While enjoying our day of celebration, a sad message came over the wireless. There has been an earthquake in Messina, Sicily. Word has it there are possibly 100,000 lives lost in the disaster. My heart goes out to the country and the families for their lost.

I shall write more later.

Your Boy,

Maurice

Le Caire.
Ascension de la grande pyramide par un touriste.

9 January 1909

Dearest Min,

Just a few lines this gloomy noon to bring you up to date. We have just finished coaling the ship, and everything is covered in coal dust. It has been such a busy time for all of us, however, we will be home in only a little over a month. I'm counting the days.

We have just learned our fleet will be splitting up and sailing in various directions. I guess there were just too many places we have to make appearances in and too little time.

We changed to the blue uniform on 2 January as the weather

cooled. We anchored at the southern end of the Suez Canal at 8:00 am on 3 January, two days ahead of schedule. We upped our speed to get to port early to receive further information and instructions about the earthquake in Sicily. When we arrived, receptions were withheld in reverence to the earthquake victims.

We've been told the Suez Canal handles almost 4,000 ships a year, but on 4 January, our fleet became the largest single group of ships in history to transit through the canal at one time. The canal is one hundred miles long and 33 to 36 feet deep, except for a large lake in the center. The breadth is around 120 feet. At times, our warships— about 75 feet wide— were very close to the embankments where the ever-present beggars loomed. We heard a British warship got stuck and had to be blown up just to resume traffic down the canal! (214)

Each ship was given a pilot to help the Captains maneuver their ships through the canal. There were about 120 pilots in all. Each pilot navigated only a short distance, and then another pilot took his place. The Captains were at the helm the entire eighteen hours steaming through the canal. The traveling speed had to be reduced to only six miles an hour. Otherwise, the "wash from their bows would injure the embankments." (216) The cost to the United States for the fleet and four auxiliaries to travel the Suez Canal totaled $150,000 (217)

Good news! I was one of 1,600 first-class sailors granted permission to go sightseeing for two days while our ships maneuvered the canal. We, along with Rear Admiral Potter of the *Vermont*, were rushed on a special train to Cairo. The train was so crowded, men were hanging out the windows, and some of us had to ride on the roof. We were invited to a banquet and a tour, one we could not refuse. We did our naval duty at the banquet, then most of us went on the outing. There were, however, a few fellows who cut up in some of the restaurants instead. As you can see, I obtained many postals for your collection during those two days.

We hired guides to help us maneuver through the beggars, thieves, and mass of people. We saw the Sphinx and had our pictures taken to show people at home that we had really visited this great wonder.

Only one ship, the *Georgia*, had a mishap while navigating the Suez. "The telegraph to one of the engines became disarranged, and the indicator suddenly marked 'full speed astern.' Those in the engine room thought some emergency had arisen and obeyed the order with alacrity. The result was that the *Georgia* poked her bow into the bank of the canal before word could be passed down to rectify the error." (215) Valuable time was lost as sailors, Arabs, camels, and horses tugged at lines attached to the battleship's stern to free her.

Our guide told us the ear of the Sphinx is four and a half feet, and the nose is five feet, seven inches! (218) We were even allowed to climb the Great Pyramid. Each step is about three feet high, and very slippery from all the tourists before us. I had to be boosted by three natives— one to push, and one to hold each of my hands— to get me to the top! I could see, carved into the stone, names of tourists from every nation. I, of course, followed suit and added my name. (219)

The old ruins that you see in the post cards date farther back than the pyramids. They are the old tombs of the first rulers of Babylon. I think the sunset scene showing an Arab at prayer at the base of the Sphinx is a very pretty scene that appeals to the student of nature in me. The natives of Egypt are very religious—many worshiping the great Sun God, Ra, as did their ancestors. I have to say the scenes in and around Cairo are the most interesting of any I have ever seen.

The Holy Carpet.

United State Atlantic Fleet
Our travels in Egypt on January 1909.

We rented donkeys and camels. (Yes, I had some photos taken of me on a camel.) While visiting Cairo, most of us exchanged our traditional flat hats for the tall, cylindrical native hat called a fez. You can see me wearing one while riding.

We rejoined our ships in Port Said after they had successfully maneuvered the canal to coal for the homeward bound fuel. (220) This was certainly a very eventful part of the cruise for me. Take care and know I send my heart.

Maurice

The American public looked forward to reading in their newspapers about the grand celebrations in Europe. To bring the fleet home so soon seemed such a waste. Sperry was not at all thrilled at the prospect of more pageants. On 5 January, while still maneuvering the canal, word came to him of an additional twelve pageants. To arrive home on time, he would have to split the fleet whether it upset anyone or not. It was decided that the "First Division would go to Naples to offer earthquake assistance and thence to Villefranche on the French Riviera for liberty. The Second Division would proceed directly to Marseilles for liberty and then on to Tangier. The Third Division would break into two units to visit Greek and Turkish ports, the Fourth would split up to visit the North African littoral—Malta, Tripoli, and Algiers." (221)

Refueling began in Port Said, on 6 January. The Department of the Navy ordered food and supplies to be directed from the fleet to Messina. The *Culgoa* was coaled first, and was commanded to go to the scene of the disaster to "deliver her remaining cargo of several hundred tons of foodstuffs." (222) The other battleships were canvassed for any available medical supplies. These supplies and six surgeons followed the *Culgoa* in the *Yankton*.]

GIBRALTAR

SAILORS FROM THE BATTLE FLEET VIEWING THE RUINS OF MESSINA, SICILY. DESTROYED BY EARTHQUAKE DEC. 28. 1908.

2 February 1909

Dearest Minnie,

And how is my loved one today? Well, I hope. And I do hope the labor troubles out there will end presto for these strikes are the worst thing that could happen to a working man. Darling, don't you think it best to go to San Diego first? I like that place, and I feel sure of prospering there. Never fear love, we will have our home all to ourselves and will live independent, believe me. Dearest, I will write Frank tomorrow.

We anchored at Gibraltar yesterday and were able to hear about the travels of the other divisions. As I told you in my last letter, each division had to visit different ports. I will try to relay the information as I heard it.

The First Division maneuvered through the Strait of Messina, traveling at only two knots because the navigational charts proved to be useless after the quake. Admiral Sperry dropped anchor in Messina

Frank was involved in labor strikes in the steel mills and ended up being black-listed for the rest of his working career.

in hopes of giving aid, but the Ambassador to Italy said the Italians resented American aid. To receive our aid would be an embarrassment before the eyes of the world. (223) The Italians wanted to handle the situation themselves to show the world they were capable. Hundreds were still starving, and I understand the papers in the states were all praising the Americans for their efforts to save Messina after the quake, so Admiral Sperry couldn't order the *Culgoa* home. You would probably know more about the reports in the papers than I do.

The First Division then berthed at Naples, but the festivities previously planned had all been canceled because of the quake. The presence of four American battleships became objectionable. All except the *Connecticut* headed for the French Riviera. Of course, the Navy wives followed the ships to the Riviera; they considered the Riviera the high point of *their* tour. (Now that would have been soft duty!) Admiral Sperry took a train to Rome to try to patch up relations with the king.

In Villefranche, the men said sailboats circled their ships and swimmers came asking to come aboard dressed in strange bathing suits. Bands played, and guns resounded from the French warships. That pageant lasted for thirteen days.

The city of Nice presented a prize of $6,000 to the *Kansas* football team after it defeated the *Minnesota* 6 to 2. It must have been a very positive visit. Thousands of people visited the ships, and several of Frenchmen— including an Army officer and a priest— tried to enlist in our Navy! Frank would have enjoyed hearing the great liberty stories some of these men shared, But I don't think I should repeat them here. The First Division left Villefranche on 27 January and headed for Gibraltar.

The Second Division went to Marseilles. There were celebrations, operas, races, balls, speeches, and luncheons. The wives who followed that Division wanted to go to Paris, so some of the officers took their wives to Paris a. The *Georgia* and the *Nebraska* went on to Tangier, arriving on 30 January. Captain Qualtrough of the *Georgia* was exhausted. When they hit stormy weather, the story goes that the

Captain stayed up all night on the bridge drinking coffee to stay alert. The next morning, when he arrived at Tangier, he drank more coffee to continue to stay awake. He managed to make it through a tea dance and a dinner before he sagged and grabbed a post for support. He was arrested on the spot for being drunk while on duty. I understand he will be court-martialed while here in Gibraltar.

On 27 January, the *Georgia* and the *Nebraska* sailed for Morocco, arriving on 30 January. Twenty-five enlisted men per ship were granted liberty. I was told one of the senior officers returned to his ship intoxicated. Later that evening, while attending a formal ball, he appeared to weave down the receiving line. He too was relieved of command, and a court-martial will be held while we are here in Gibraltar. I think we all need to be back in the good old US of A.

The Fourth Division also divided: the *Kentucky* went on to Tripoli to spend two days, arriving 13 January; the *Wisconsin* and the *Kearsarge* arrived at Malta on 14 January; the *Illinois* received orders to go to Messina to search for the bodies of the American Consul Arthur S. Cheney and his wife. About four hundred men went ashore in Messina.

The stories we are hearing about Messina are just awful. There are between 60,000 to 80,000 people still buried in the rubble. So many people died in such a small city, because so many people were crowded together in every house. We've been told that there are looters and crowds of people everywhere. Our men recovered eight adults and three children who had lived for eighteen days after the quake. One friend laughingly reported they dug out three men who had landed in some garlic and cognac and didn't seem a bit shaken. (224)

Captain Qualtrough was brought back to the United States as a prisoner on his own ship, even though his doctor said he was not drunk on the night in question. After a few months, Qualtrough was vindicated and retired with the rank of Commodore.

Reggio Calabria dopo il terremoto del 28 dicembre 1908.
Accampamento della Comp. Allievi Guardie di Finanza di Maddaloni presso la Stazione Succursale.

3

la catastrofe di Messina
Via Garibaldi e Palazzo del Prefetto

4

They tell us very few buildings are left standing, some with only the framework. All around the outskirts of the city, tents have been erected to house the now homeless people. It must look similar to the San Francisco earthquake of '06. The men reported seeing many streets with huge zigzag fissures blocks long. After about five hours of searching, our men found the bodies of the consul and his wife. Once their goal was accomplished, they returned to their ship.

The crew of the *Culgoa* is going to remain to help with other relief crews. The *Illinois* reached Malta on 17 January, joining the men from the *Kearsarge*. The *Kentucky* joined the division arriving from Tripoli.

Scene at Algiers, Africa, during the visit of the American Fleet.

The Fourth Division then steamed to Algiers. All crews were able to go ashore except those from the *Kearsarge* because they were still being punished for stealing. Just yesterday, the captain of the *Kearsarge* gave up his command here in Gibraltar. According to those I have spoken to, the petty thievery I mentioned earlier finally got the better of him.

The Third Division sent the *Missouri* and the *Ohio* to Athens arriving in time for the Greek New Year celebrations. It was a little difficult for the officers, however, because there were so few of them. They could not trade duties to the luncheons, dinners, and other celebrations, so they all had to attend all the festivities. They arrived here in Gibraltar quite an exhausted bunch.

The *Virginia* and the *Louisiana* were sent to Beirut. When we arrived, we found Beirut ridden with the plague. Within the hour, we had come about and were on our way to Smyrna, Turkey. I was able to pick up some very nice cards in Turkey of the scenery and living conditions of the people to share with you. I had a really nice time. I visited some of the ruins and took some pictures I want Frank to see. I was very impressed with the ruins of the Greek Theatre, built entirely from marble. I only wish you and Frank could have been there with me. I was also able to buy some cute souvenirs for you, Min. I will send them to you when we get home.

On the very calm and sunny day of 19 January, we docked in Smyrna. We were all startled when our ship began rocking for no apparent reason. We quickly learned of another earthquake that killed eight people. Panic ran through Smyrna, and the festivities were canceled.

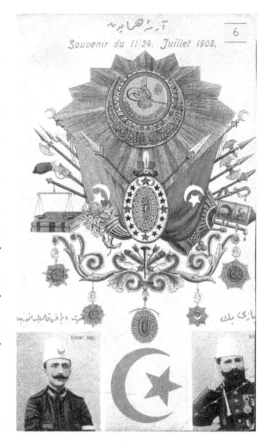

By 31 January, using a powerful glass, we could see the mighty rock of Gibraltar. "Prudential has the strength of Gibraltar," so says an American advertisement for the insurance company. The old salts tried to fool the minds of the young enlisted men by telling them whoever discovers the painted sign on the rock first would receive, free of charge, several shares in the Prudential Life Insurance Company. So many of the new enlisted men spent a lot of time looking for a sign that never existed! (225) As we got closer to the rock, we saw guns everywhere.

Russian, French, and British ships, as well as a large audience, waited on the shore to greet us. The gun salutes were given, and the bands played the anthems. As soon as we anchored, bumboats flocked around us selling their wares for "special American Fleet prices." We have certainly experienced *that* quite a bit during this tour. They're suggesting that the American sailor can still be fooled, (226) but I think everyone has learned that isn't necessarily true at this point in the cruise.

No liberties are to be given to the enlisted men here in Gibraltar. The officers can go ashore to attend the banquets, balls, and receptions, and tour the town on their own. Yesterday the cry was heard once again: "all hands coal ship!" There is a different feeling about the chore this time. This is the coal that will carry us home! I will write later after we are on our way to Hampton Roads. It won't be long now.

With all my heart,

Maurice

GIBRALTAR
View of the Harbour with the British, American and Russian Fleets
31. January 1909.

GIBRALTAR
View of the Harbour and Part of the American and Russian Fleets

8

Another officer was relieved of his command when he suffered a nervous breakdown on the *Kentucky*. Back in Washington, it was agreed the age of the commanding officers would be lowered so younger men would be commanding the ships, thus avoiding so many mishaps.

Food was needed for the fleet as the *Culgoa* as she had given all of her stores to Messina. The fleet was depending on the supply ship, *Republic*, which had left with the needed supplies from New York to meet the First Division in Naples. But on 23 January the liner *Florida* running through fog on the New Jersey coast rammed into the *Republic*. Both ships sank. The pay Inspector paid an unconfirmed amount ($150,000, says one source, (227), $36,670, states another source) (228) to a slaughterhouse in Marseilles to replace the meat lost. The meat was given to the *Culgoa* to take to Gibraltar. Once in Gibraltar, it was discovered the meat was contaminated. The British garrisons at Gibraltar offered stores of beef and hard tack to hold the men until they returned home.

Each ship required between 1,200 to 1,600 tons of coal for the trip to Hampton Roads. "The upper decks of the *Illinois* were so full of coal that there was no room for men to fall in at quarters." (229) The last ship to complete coaling was the *Kentucky*. A few hours later, on the morning of 6 February 1909, the battleships formed a single line, and left Gibraltar with the bands playing "Home Sweet Home."

New York wanted the fleet to conclude the cruise at their port feeling they could celebrate with superior entertainment for the finale. New Orleans also wanted the fleet to attend Mardi Gras. For once, the Department of the Navy said, No. Let's get these men home!

Homeward Bound

U.S.S. KEARSARGE

MEET ME AT HAMPTON ROADS, FEB. 21, 1909.

23 February 1909

Dearest Minnie,

Your dear sweet note with cards and Valentine awaited me in Hampton Roads. Many, many thanks. Oh, how I long for the moment when we are together. If I were only there with you—well, you know the result for I would be perfectly wild. I think someone else would be ditto when I got through teasing.

The trip from Gibraltar to Hampton Roads was not an easy one. On 8 February, during the middle of our drills, a sharp report was heard, indicating a man overboard, was fired by the *Louisiana*. Being directly behind her, we followed suit. Torches were lit, and life-buoys were lowered into the water. Searchlights from the entire fleet lit up to locate the missing man. The *Louisiana* launched a lifeboat and picked up a buoy, but there was no sight of the missing sailor. A call to muster— "All hands"— was heard through the squadron. It was eventually determined there had been no man overboard! (230) Never a time to get lazy in this man's Navy! Drills were resumed while the weather remained good.

Unfortunately, the weather didn't stay calm. Instead, it took a turn for the worse. Valentine's Day became very memorable indeed. The *Illinois*, the *Kentucky*, and my ship all lost lifeboats. By 19 February, I felt the seas were almost as bad as the typhoon between Manila and Japan! For several days, we could not utilize tables to eat our meals.

At times, I saw our stern rising so high out of the water that I could actually see the huge propellers, and for that instant, the ship would shake from stem to stern. (231) Not an experience I want to repeat. Even though these last few days at sea became some of the most difficult of the entire trip, we never lost formation! (232)

About 1,200 miles from Hampton on the morning of 17 February, we saw a trail of smoke off the starboard bow. The *Main*, the *New Hampshire*, the *Mississippi*, the *Idaho* and the *Salem* and their cruisers were there to welcome us home. These ships were all painted the war color of drab. The *Mississippi* and the *Idaho* had a new type of mast resembling huge oil towers (233) or upside down woven trash baskets. What a beautiful sight to behold. It's only when you have been away from home for such a long time that you can fully appreciate the dear land which we have had the honor to serve. (234)

We no longer were the Big Sixteen, heading for home. We had become the Big Twenty-One!

Some of the excitement faded that afternoon when another 'man overboard' was flashed from the *New Hampshire*. The next day I learned another man had been lost to the seas.

The *Chester* joined us on 18 February. The *Montana*, the *North Carolina* and the *Birmingham* welcomed us on 19 February. By that evening, thank goodness, the seas began to calm. What a beautiful sight we must have been, the Big Twenty-Five!

On 21 February, we dropped anchor off Cape Henry working all night to apply the last coat of white paint so we could pass the Presidential inspection the next day.

Even though we were all exhausted, yesterday was a grand day indeed. The day started with a low fog obstructing our view. As soon as the *Mayflower* was spotted, the *Connecticut* gave her 21-gun salute, and the fog lifted. We saw President Roosevelt and Mr. Taft standing on the bridge waving a welcome. The *Vermont* added her 21-guns. At that point, with all the smoke, we couldn't even get a glimpse of the shore we had so longed to see! Every ship, in turn, fired her guns in salute. As we steamed close to shore, we heard a band playing that wonderful melody "There's no Place Like Home." Such a delight, it brought tears to my eyes. Once the smoke cleared, we saw banners and flags hanging everywhere awaiting our entrance.

There was a brief reception for the Admirals and the commanding officers aboard the *Mayflower*, after which the President boarded each of the four flagships and made a speech receiving standing ovations. All the while, thousands of small craft gathered in and around us. Greetings resonated from the crowds on shore from whistles, fog horns, sirens. Bands played on every ship. What a celebration! All the battleships gave a 21-gun salute for the President and another one to commemorate Washington's Birthday as well as our triumphal return home; a 2,000-gun salute!

I know for the next two days there will be presidential balls, receptions, Navy League Dinners, and of course a huge celebration parade. Most of us had to return to our ships to begin the arduous task of coaling. We are all waiting for President Roosevelt to go back to Washington so we can

6

...ING IN FRONT OF THE NAVAL Y.M.C.A. BUILDING,
...LK, VA. AFTER THE PARADE, FEB. 27, 1908.

get our leave papers in order. Wives and girlfriends for many in this fleet were waiting for them, staying at the Chamberlin Hotel. I understand they had to put cots in the hallways to accommodate everyone. For all too many of us, this is just another port where our loved ones are not here to greet us.

Time is not long now until I board the train straight to my girl. Dearest, if this unfeeling paper could only talk it would make your dear heart glad for it would tell you of the continual thoughts of my heart. They are of you, precious girl, and always will be. I love you. I love you. I love you, Darling. I always will love you.

Maurice

"What the American public saw was the successful completion, with few apparent difficulties, of the longest fleet cruise ever undertaken by any navy. That ships of the fleet might not have been properly designed as a result of faulty organization within the Navy Department, that the Navy lacked the essential logistic support of a healthy merchant marine, and the senior officers of the fleet were too old and, despite their advanced age, too inexperienced in high command—these were fine points often ignored in favor of the pomp and ceremony, the orations and ovations, that attended the battleships as they proceeded on their great voyage."(235)

Only a few hours after the final ceremony, the Navy yard workers began to strip off the fancywork and most of the bridgework. Within a week, all sculptured ornaments had been scraped off of prows, the hulls had been painted gray, and new

Dec. 16th 1908 Around the World Feb 22 1909

7

"SOUVENIR RETURN OF THE FLEET."
NORFOLK, VA.

lattice masts were installed to replace the pole masts to support fire control stations. "These measures which permanently altered the appearance of the fleet, symbolized not just the end of the cruise and the Great White Fleet, but also the end of an era in American Naval development." (236)

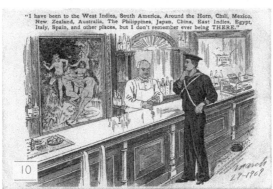

This was the last great hurrah for the age of the white battleships,
with their buff masts and high diplomacy on the seas.

Maurice completed his tour of duty on board the *USS Virginia* on 8 March 1911. The postcards, letters, and gifts continued between Maurice, Minnie, and Frank while aboard ship. Minnie and Maurice made elaborate plans for their future together in San Diego growing fonder of one another with each card. Maurice was confident his skills as a laborer and a musician would support Minnie in the manner to which she had become accustomed. With each card, he counted the months and days until his return to California and his sweetheart.

During the last months of duty, Maurice must have received a letter from his mother in Tompkinsville. He states on a card to Minnie dated March 29, 1910, "What I don't know is what to do about going home to see the place and Mother. I fear for the results." Maurice did go home after his tour before seeing Minnie. On a card addressed to Frank dated March 31, 1911, "I am home at last and am awful glad to be here . . . Mother was overjoyed to see me as I was to see her. My dear Mother talks a heap about you and The Girl, she will write soon . . . Frank, if I was to go to each home where I have been invited it would take me a year to make the rounds. I only wish you were here with me and mother. I can't say now just when I will see you, but I hope it won't be too long."

On 11 May 1911, Minnie received a card from one of her cousins: "I don't blame you a bit—no mother-in-law for mine. I wish I knew where to find a nice one; they're just about as scarce as hen's teeth I think." And then on 17 June, "Dear Thing, Hope you are through pinning these days— 'Old girls' can't afford to—we'll save ourselves for another day and all things come to those who wait."

Neither Minnie nor Frank married. After 1911, Frank experienced many disappointments. He never realized his dream of establishing a photography business, and he had difficulty getting a job as a machinist. He had been blacklisted because of his involvement with the unions. Aunt Emma moved Frank and Minnie to Santa Ana when their money became scarce, however, she continued to support them even after her death.

At the date of this writing, I have been unable to locate any further information about John Maurice Blair. If anyone reading this story is able to provide additional facts about his subsequent life, I would appreciate hearing from you. You can contact me through my website listed below.

Leslie Compton

LeslieCompton.com
Author, Instructor, Speaker

STATISTICS

1. $20,000 a day was needed to keep each ship in running order

2. Twenty-nine cities gave parties for the Fleet. Total costs in these cities for entertainment and decorations: $11,000,000, China was the biggest spender

3. Melbourne, Australia held the record for the number of functions in on day.

4. Australia had the largest crowds.

5. Britain and France became our allies.

6. Relations with Germany would never be the same.

7. President Taft spent millions of dollars to repair the damaged feelings in China.

8. First Fleet to travel 46,000 miles, to visit six continents and twenty-six countries.

9. The Fleet carried more than 14,000 men, consumed 435,000 tons of coal, which cost, $1,967,553 and wore out 250 shovels per ship.

10. The Fleet used 100,000 pounds of saluting powder; about thirty times that in the Spanish-American War. Used 360 guns in total. One single firing from all guns cost the navy $50,000; President Roosevelt's salary for one year!

11. No other country could afford to burn $20,000,000 for such a cruise.

12. Admiral Evans began a lecture tour in a wheelchair delivering "sarcastic remarks about prestige and the President." (p.301,1)

13. The weakness in the cruise: The reliance of foreign colliers, which was not solved until liquid fuel replaced coal.

14. Nation after nation thanked the United States for inspiring them to enlarge their navies, ordering new battleships.

15. The cost of the Fleet was $96,606,000. It ranged from $4,621,000 to build the *Illinois* to $7,677,000 to build the *Connecticut*.

ENDNOTES

Prologue

(1)   *US Navy 1908, Bluejacket's Manual*, 358

Historical Background

(2)   Wimmel, *Theodore Roosevelt and the Great White Fleet*, 8

(3)   Ibid., 34

(4)   Ibid., 4

(4a)   Reckner, editing, 2001

(5)   Reckner, *Teddy Roosevelt's Great White Fleet*

(6)   Baer, *One Hundred Years of Sea Power*

(7)   Winmel, *Theodore Roosevelt and the Great White Fleet*, 37

(8)   Ibid., 81

(9)   Ibid, 106

(10)   Hart, *The Great White Fleet*, XI

(10a) Hart, *The Great White Fleet*,18

(11)   US Naval Institute, *Around the World with the Fleet*

(12)   Hart, *The Great White Fleet*, 18 & 19

(13)   Winmel, *Theodore Roosevelt and the Great White Fleet*, 193

(14)   Ibid., 6

(15)   Hart, *The Great White Fleet*, 23

(16)   Baer, *One Hundred Years of Sea Power*, 41

(17)   Winmel, *Theodore Roosevelt and the Great White Fleet*, 223

(16a) Hart, *Great White Fleet*, 46

(18)   Winmel, *Theodore Roosevelt and the Great White Fleet*, 223

(18a) Marolda, *Theodore Roosevelt, The U.S. Navy and the Spanish American War*, 97

(19)   Hart, *Great White Fleet*, 30

Hampton Roads

(20)   Reckner, *Teddy Roosevelt's Great White Fleet*, 21

(21)   Hart, *The Great White Fleet*

(22)   Matthews, *With the Battle Fleet*

(23)   Jones, *From the Atlantic to the Pacific*, 95

(24)   Hart, *The Great White Fleet*

(25)   Ibid., 69

(26)   Ibid., 69

(27)   Ibid., 71

Trinidad

(28) Jones, *From the Atlantic to the Pacific*, 29

(29) US Navy 1908, Bluejacket's Manual, 59

(30) Ibid.

(31) Hart, *The Great White Fleet*, 81

(32) "At Liberty", *Harper's Weekly*, 13

(33) Ibid.

(34) Matthews, *With the Battle Fleet*, 38

(35) Ibid. 44

(36) Miller, *Around the World with the Battle Fleet*, 24

(37) *The Random House Dictionary*

(38) Matthews, *With the Battle Fleet*, 43

(39) Miller, *Around the World with the Battle Fleet*, 25

En Route to Rio

(40) Matthews, *With the Battle Fleet*, 57

(41) Hart, *The Great White Fleet*, 93

(42) "One Night with the Fleet", *Cosmopolitan*, 461,

(43) Jones, *From the Atlantic to the Pacific*, 42

(44) Ibid., 43

(45) Matthews, *With the Battle Fleet*, 66

(46) Jones, *From the Atlantic to the Pacific*, 43

(47) Matthews, *With the Battle Fleet*, 76

(48) Jones, *From the Atlantic to the Pacific*, 45

(49) Ibid., 45

(50) Ibid., 47

(51) Hart, *The Great White Fleet*, 92

Rio de Janeiro

(52) Matthews, *With The Battle Fleet*, 102

(53) Ibid., 104

(54) Ibid., 101

(55) Hart, *The Great White Fleet*

(56) Miller, *Around the World with the Battle Fleet*, 30

(57) Matthews, *The Great White Fleet*, 111

(58) Ibid., 113

(59) Matthews, *With the Battle Fleet*, 127

(60) Hart, *The Great White Fleet*, 115

En Route to Puntas Arenas, Chile

(61)   Matthews, *With the Battle Fleet*, 178

(62)   Hart, *The Great White Fleet*, 130

(63)   Matthews, *With the Battle Fleet*, 156

(64)   Reckner, *Teddy Roosevelt's Great White Fleet*, 46

(65)   Ibid., 46

Callao, Peru

(66)   Reckner, *Teddy Roosevelt's Great White Fleet*, 46

(67)   Ibid., 46

(68)   Miller, *Around the World with the Battle Fleet*

(69)   Hart, *The Great White Fleet*, 139

(70)   Ibid., 140

(71)   Ibid.

(72)   Miller, *Around the World with the Battle Fleet*, 43

(73)   Hart, *The Great White Fleet*, 146

(74)   Ibid.,145

(75)   "At Liberty", *Harper's Weekly*, 13

(76)   Miller, *Around the World with The Battle Fleet*, 48

Magdalena Bay

(77)   Matthews, *With the Battle Fleet*, 230

(78)   Jones, *From the Atlantic to the Pacific*, 101

(79)   Ibid., 101

(80)   Ibid., 105

(81)   Hart, *The Great White Fleet*, 155

(82)   Ibid., 155

(83)   Ibid., 157

California

(84)   Weldon, *The Great White Fleet Visits Santa Barbara*, 14

(85)   Reckner, *Teddy Roosevelt's Great White Fleet*, 56

(86)   *Associated Press*, San Diego

(87)   Reckner, *Teddy Roosevelt's Great White Fleet*, 57

(88)   *Morning Press,* Santa Barbara

(89)   *Associated Press,* San Diego

(90)   *Morning Press,* Santa Barbara *(no date)*

(91)   Ind*ependent*, Santa Barbara

(92)   Winmel, *Theodore Roosevelt and the Great White Fleet*, 230

(93)   Matthews, *With The Battle Fleet*, 264

(94)   *Morning Press*, Santa Barbara, April 19, 1908

(95)   Weldon, *The Great White Fleet Visits Santa Barbara*, 12

(96)   Ibid., 15

(97)   Ibid.

(98)   Hart, *The Great White Fleet*, 24

(99)   Weldon, *The Great White Fleet Visits Santa Barbara*, 12

(100)   Hart, *The Great White Fleet*, 166

(101)   Brantingham, *UCSB Book Captures the Great White Fleet Visit*

(102)   Weldon, *The Great White Fleet Visits Santa Barbara*, 13

(103)   Hart, *The Great White Fleet*, 166

(104)   "Peace Voyage of the United States White Fleet" Book Club of California

(105)   Hart, *The Great White Fleet*

(106)   G. P. Putnam, *Outlook Magazine* used in SF article in quotes, 7

(107)   "The Second Biggest Thing to Hit San Francisco", *San Francisco Chronicle*, 2

(108)   Hart, *The Great White Fleet*, 167

(109)   *San Francisco Examiner*, Editorial page, May 8, 1908

(110)   "The Second Biggest Thing to Hit San Francisco", *San Francisco Chronicle*, 2

(111)   "With the Enlisted Men", *San Francisco Examiner*, May 8, 1908

(112)   *San Francisco Chronicle*, May 12, 1908

(113)   "The Second Biggest Thing to Hit San Francisco", *San Francisco Chronicle*, 2

(114)   "Peace Voyage of the Untied States White Fleet", *The Book Club of California*

(115)   "The Second Biggest Thing to Hit San Francisco", *San Francisco Chronicle*, 2

(116)   *San Francisco Examiner*, May 9, 1908

(117)   Willing, *Letters From the Great White Fleet*, 17

(118)   Ibid.

(119)   Ibid.

(120)   Reckner, *Teddy Roosevelt's Great White Fleet*, 83

Washington

(121)   Seattle, Washington, *Bellingham Herald*, May 23, 1908

(122)   "Atlantic Fleet Anchors in Seattle's harbor", *Seattle Star*, 1

(123)   Ibid.

(124)   Seattle, Washington, *Seattle Star*, March 27, 1908, 1

(125)   Ibid.

(126)   Ibid.

(127)   Reckner, *Teddy Roosevelt's Great White Fleet*, 86

(128)   "Great White Fleet Gave Americans New Confidence" *Seattle Post-Intelligencer*, May 26, 1983

(129)   San Francisco Municipal Reports, 1907-1908

(130)   Reckner, *Teddy Roosevelt's Great White Fleet*, 140

Hawai'i

(131)   Reckner, *Teddy Roosevelt's Great White Fleet*, 88

(132)   Matthews, *Back to Hampton Roads*, 18

(133)   Ibid.

(134)   Reckner, *Teddy Roosevelt's Great White Fleet*, 89

(135)   Ibid., 90

New Zealand

(136) Miller, *Around the World with the Battle Fleet*, 79

(137) Reckner, *Teddy Roosevelt's Great White Fleet*, 140

(138) Ibid.

(139) Hart, *The Great White Fleet*, 186

(140) Reckner, *Teddy Roosevelt's Great White Fleet*, 94

(141) Miller, *Around the World with the Battle Fleet*, 87

(142) Matthews, *Back to Hampton Roads*, 36

(143) Reckner, *Teddy Roosevelt's Great White Fleet*, 95

(144) Postcards from Birdie to Alvin from SF Library

Australia

(145) Miller, *Around the World with the Battle Fleet*, 104

(146) Ibid., 104

(147) Ibid., 105

(148) Ibid., 105

(149) Willing, *Letters From the Great White Fleet*, 30

(150) "Visit to Australia of the Fleet of the United States of America", Sydney, 20-27 August 1908,1

(151) Matthews, *Back to Hampton Roads*, 71

(152) Reckner, *Teddy Roosevelt's Great White Fleet*, 98

(153) Ibid., 99

(154) *The Age,* Sydney, Australia, August 31, 1908, p.8

(155) "Writing Home", *Argus*, Sydney, Australia, September 3, 1908, 8

(156) *Argus*, Sydney, Australia, September 2, 1908, 8

(157) *The Age*, Sydney, Australia, September 2, 1908, 7

(158) Matthews, *Back to Hampton Roads*, 131

(159) "March of Sailors and Marines", *The Age*, September 1, 1908, 9

(160) "The March to Melbourne", *The Australian*, September 5, 1908, 620

(161) Miller, *Around the World with the Battle Fleet*, 148

(162) "Unlucky Kangaroos", *Argus*, September 1, 1908, 6

(163) Miller, *Around the World with the Battle Fleet,* 155

(164) Reckner, *Teddy Roosevelt's Great White Fleet*, 101

(165) "The Fleet's Return", *Literary Digest*, 327

(166) Matthews, *Back to Hampton Roads*, 128, 129

Manila

(167) Matthews, *Back to Hampton Roads*, 157

Japan

(168) Hart, *The Great White Fleet*, 217

(169) Matthews, *Back to Hampton Roads*, 178

(170) Ibid., 173

(171) US Naval Institute, *Around the World with the Fleet 1907-1908*

(172) Matthews, *Back to Hampton Roads*, 189

(173) Reckner, *Teddy Roosevelt's Great White Fleet*, 114

(174) Ibid., 114

(175) Ibid, 114

(176) Matthews, Back to Hampton Roads, 191

(177) Miller, *Around the World with the Battle Fleet*, 192

(178) Hart, *The Great White Fleet*, 225

(179) Miller, *Around the World with the Battle Fleet*, 201

(180) Ibid., 206

(181) Ibid., 201

(182) Ibid., 230

(183) Hart, *The Great White Fleet*

(184) Reckner, *Teddy Roosevelt's Great White Fleet*

(185) Miller, *Around the world with the Battle Fleet*, 216-217

(186) Matthews, *Back to Hampton Roads*, 206

(187) Reckner, *Teddy Roosevelt's Great White Fleet*, 115

(188) Winmel, *Theodore Roosevelt and the Great White Fleet*, 240

China

(189) Hart, *The Great White Fleet*

(190) Hart, *The Great White Fleet*, 239

(191) Hart, *The Great White Fleet*, 248

(192) Reckner, *Teddy Roosevelt's Great White Fleet*, 120

(193) Hart, *The Great White Fleet*, 247

Back to Manila

(194) Matthews, *Back to Hampton Roads*, 229

(195) Ibid., 254

(196) Miller, *Around the World with the Battle Fleet*, 260

(197) Ibid., 266

(198) Ibid., 277-278

(199) Ibid., 278

(200) Ibid., 278

Colombo, Ceylon

(201) Miller, *Around the World with the Battle Fleet*, 297

(202) Ibid., 281

(203) Ibid., 281

(204) Matthews, *Back to Hampton Roads*, 261

(205) Miller, *Around the World with the Battle Fleet*, 287-288

(206) Ibid., 291

(207) Ibid., 297-298

(208) Ibid., 298

Suez

(209)   Hart, *The Great White Fleet*, 269

(210)   Ibid.

(211)   Miller, *Around the World with the Battle Fleet*, 300

(212)   Matthews, *Back to Hampton Roads*

(213)   Miller, *Around the World with the Battle Fleet*, 302

(214)   Matthews, *Back to Hampton Roads*, 279

(215)   Miller, *Around the World with the Battle Fleet*, 282

(216)   Miller, *Around the World with the Battle Fleet*, 326

(217)   Hart, *The Great White Fleet*

(218)   Miller, *Around the World with the Battle Fleet*, 326

(219)   Ibid., 311

(220)   Ibid., 315

(221)   Reckner, *Teddy Roosevelt's Great White Fleet*, 147

(222)   Ibid., 145

Gibraltar

(223)   Hart, *The Great White Fleet*, 281

(224)   Willing, *Letters from the Great White Fleet*, 45

(225)   Miller, *Around the World with the Battle Fleet*, 340

(226)   Ibid., 343

(227)   Hart, *The Great White Fleet*

(228)   Reckner, *Teddy Roosevelt's Great White Fleet*

(229)   Ibid., 152

Back to Hampton Roads

(230)   Miller, *Around the World with the Battle Fleet*

(231)   Miller, *Around the World with the Battle Fleet*, 356

(232)   Matthews, *Back to Hampton Roads*, 291

(233)   Miller, *Around the World with the Battle Fleet*, 354

(234)   Ibid., 351

(235)   Reckner, *Teddy Roosevelt's Great White Fleet*, xi

(236)   Reckner, *Teddy Roosevelt's Great White Fleet*, 156

BIBLIOGRAPHY

Published Government Documents

----. Bureau of Navigation. *Men on Board Ships of the Atlantic Fleet Bound for the Pacific December 16, 1907: With Home Addresses in the United States.* Washington: GPO, 1908

----. Bureau of Navigation. *Information Relative to the Voyage of the United States Atlantic Fleet Around the World, December 16, 1907 to February 22, 1909.* Washington: GPO, 1910

----. The Naval Institute. *Bluejacket's Manual, United States Navy 1908.*   U.S. Naval Academy Library, Annapolis, MD, 1908

Unpublished Works

"Alvin". Postcards sent to Miss Birdie Wedding, 1908

Blair, Maurice. Postcards sent to Minnie Camp, 1907 - 1910

Richards, Theodore Wright, Medical Corps, USN "Great White Fleet Scrapbook, 1908-1909". From Los Angles April, 1908 to Virginia, February, 1909 U. S. Naval Academy Library, Annapolis, MD

Books

Alden, John D. *The American Steel Navy.* Annapolis: Naval Institute Press, 1972

Around the World with the Fleet, 1907-1909: A Pictorial Log of the Cruise. Annapolis: Naval Institute Press, 1929

Baer, George W. *One Hundred Years of Sea Power, the United States Navy, 1890 – 1990,* Published by Stanford University, 1994

Beale, Howard K. *Theodore Roosevelt and the Rise of America to World Power.* Baltimore: Johns Hopkins Press, 1956

Carter, S. *The Incredible Great White Fleet.* New York: Collier's Press, 1971

Hart, Robert A. *The Great White Fleet: Its Voyage Around the World,* Boston: Little, Brown, 1965

Jones, Robert D. *With the American Fleet from the Atlantic to the Pacific.* Seattle: Harrison, 1908

Matthews, Franklin, *With the Battlefleet: Cruise of the Sixteen Battleships of the United States Atlantic Fleet from Hampton Roads to the Golden Gate, December 1907-May 1908.* New York: B.W. Hebsch, 1908

Back to Hampton Roads: Cruise of the United States Atlantic Fleet from San Francisco to Hampton Roads, July 7, 1908-February 22, 1909. New York: B. W. Huebsch, 1909.

Miller, Chief Turret Captain Roman J. *Around the World with the Battleships.* 3rd ed. Chicago: A. C. McClurg, 1910

Reckner, James R. *Teddy Roosevelt's Great White Fleet*, Annapolis: Naval Institute Press, 1988

Weldon, Hugh J. *Noticias*, Santa Barbara Historical Society, Fiesta Edition, Vol. VI, No. 2, Summer, 1960

Willing, Peter. *Letters From the Great White Fleet by Edward Shippen Willing, U.S.M.C.* Co: Peter Willing 1995

Wimmel, Kenneth, *Theodore Roosevelt and the Great White Fleet American Sea Power Comes of Age.* Washington-London, 1998 (look up title)

Articles

"Admiral Evans and the Armor Belt Problem." *Outlook 88* (4 April 1908): 758

"The American Fleet at Melbourne." *Collier's Magazine* 42, No. 5 (24 October 1908): 4

"At Liberty: Adventures in a Friendly Port with the Shore patrol During the Homecoming Run of the Battleship Feet." *Harper's Weekly,* Vol. 52, No.2681 (5 May 1908): 13-16

"The Battleship Fleet in Australian Waters." *Colliers Magazine*, Vol.42, No.3 (10 October 1908): 16-17

"The Battleship Fleet in Japan." *Collier's Magazine* Vol. 42, No.10 (28 November 1908): 16-17

"Blue Jacket Stories." *Cassier's Magazine* Vol. 41, No. 25 (12 September 1908): 19

"The Bull Fight at Lima." *Cassier's Magazine* Vol. 41, No. 6 (2 May 1908): 18

"Coaling the Pacific Fleet with Foreign Ships." *Literary Digest* Vol. 35, No. 15 (12 October 1907): 514-15

"The Coming of the Fleet." *Sunset Magazine*, Vol. XIX, No. 6 (October 1907): 509-510, 522

"The Fleet's Return." *Literary Digest* Vol. 38, No. 9 (27 February 1909):326-27

"The Joys of Target Practice." *Cassier's Magazine*, Vol. 41, No. 6 (2 May 1908): 8

"One Night with the Big Fleet: An Incident of the Cruise." *Cosmopolitan*,   Vol. 46, (March 1908): 460-465

"Work and Play of the Fleet." *Harper's Weekly*, Vol. 52, No.152666 (25 January 1908): 10-12

"The World Cruise of the American Battleship Fleet, 1907-1909." *Pacific Historical Review*, Vol. 1 No. 4 (December 1932): 389-422

Newspapers

Age (Melbourne)

Argus (Melbourne)

Associated Press (San Diego)

Auckland Star

Bellingham Herald

Santa Barbara Independent

Santa Barbara's News

Melbourne Herald

Morning Press (Santa Barbara)

New York Times

San Francisco Chronicle

San Francisco Examiner

Seattle Post-Intelligencer

Seattle Star

Sydney Bulletin

Washington Post

Pamphlets

"Official Program Californian's Welcome to the Fleet", May 1908. The California Promotion Committee for Reception of the Fleet

"Peace Voyage of the United States White Fleet" Number Nine in the series of Keepsakes West Coast Expositions and Gals. The Book Club of California, 1970

"Welcome to Our Fleet", The Official Program in Seattle

POSTCARD LIST

The postcard descriptions followed by (L) are from the collection of Les Cowman of Victoria, Australia. The postcards followed by (S) are from Dr. Steve Levine's collection

Postcard of Minnie Camp in her buggy was taken by Frank Camp in front of their home in Kern City, California.

Historical Background

1. Hahana, "Main soon after the wreck." Tarjeta Postal Card, Cuba

2. Peace talks, Ruso-Japanese Peace Commission, Aug. 1905

3. "Fighting Bob" Admiral Robert D. Evens, U. S. Navy, Published by the American News Company, New York.

Hampton Roads

1. "Warships at anchor in front of the Chamberlin", Private mailing card with an undivided back

2. "The Nations Pride", Flag series number 710, copyright 1908 by Julius Bien & Co. N.Y.

3. "Uncle Sam's Personally Conducted Tour of the World" Copyright 1908 by Middlesex Company, Middletown, Conn. (L)

4. Battle ship, *USS Virginia*, Compliments of the Prudential Insurance Company of America

5. "Uncle Sam's Warships", Undivided card, "Copyright applied for, Grove Hall Press, Boston, Mass.

6. Original Photo; Watching the Fleet steam from Hampton Roads (L)

7. "U.S. Battleship Fleet leaving Hampton Roads on its 'around-the-world-cruise.'" Published by L.E. Lines Music Co., Springfield, MO. On the front of the card reads: "The most severe test to which a player piano can be subjected is aboard a ship, yet the officers and sailors of over 50 U. S. and foreign Battleships have purchased Autopianos. . . . During the famous cruise around the world the American Fleet nearly every Battleship possessed an 'Autopiano' for the amusement and education of the officers and crew. . ."

8. A foldout postcard showing all sixteen ships in maneuvers leaving Hampton Roads. Copyright 1908, Continental Art Co., Chicago (L)

9. Original Photo, "Fleet leaving Hampton Roads, Dec. 16, 1907"

10. "Onward and onward the Fleet goes round wherever you go Old Glory's now found." Copyright by Taylor Art Co., 1908

11. Original Photo showing the temporary stage built on deck for entertainment, "A Minstrel Show on Board"

Trinidad

1.   Original Photo, after Coaling
2.   "Wash Day", Published by H. H. Stratton, Chattanooga, Tenn.
3.   "American sailors ashore at Port of Spain. Trinidad Christmas Day, 1908", Published by H. H. Stratton
4.   "Coaling ship from a collier" – Original Photo
5.   "The suburbs of Trinidad Christmas Day, 1908", Published by H. H. Stratton
6.   "After Coaling"- Original Photo

En Route to Rio

1.   *USS Virginia*, a series of postcards showing the ships and their captains
2.   "Neptune's own band"- Original Photo
3.   "Neptune and his staff" - Original Photo
4.   "Crossing the line, January 1st – the Initiation", Published by H. H. Stratton #2570
5.   The initiation- Original Photo
6.   "Initiated"; "I got mine" – Crossing the Equator, Published by the Middlesex Company, Middletown, Conn.

Rio de Janeiro

1.   "The Y.M.C.A. Bureau of Information", Rio de Janeiro, Brazil, #2575, Published by H. H. Stratton
2.   "American sailors Ashore at Rio de Janeiro, Brazil, Jan 15, 1908", Published by H. H. Stratton
3.   "Sailor Boys reading letters from home." Metropolitan News and Publishing company, Boston, Mass.

Punta Arenas, Chile

1.   "The Atlantic Fleet passing through the Straits of Magellan, February 8, 1908" #2574, Published by H. H. Stratton
2.   U. S. Navy – A Midnight attack in the Straights of Magellan" Published by Karl Lewis (L)
3.   "The Stars and Stripes Forever", Flag "series" #715

Callao, Peru

1.   Magellan Straits - Published by Wolfe's Schnapps (L)

2. "Landing of the U. S. Sailors, the 25 of February of 1908, Callao Peru", Published by E. Polack, Schneider, Lima

3. "Awaiting the Arrival of the American Fleet, Callao, Peru" (L)

4. Callao, Peru, Published by E. Polack –Schneider, Lima

5. "5,000 American sailors at Bull Fight in Lima, Peru, Feb. 24, 1909" Published by H. H. Stratton

6. "Bull fight, Lima, Peru in honor of U. S. Atlantic Fleet" Original photo

7. "Bull fight Lima, Peru, in honor of the U. S. Fleet", Original Photo

8. "Bull fight in Lima, Peru in honor of the visit of the American Fleet, Feb. 24, 1908", Published by H. H. Stratton

Magdalena Bay

1. "Paso Robles Hot Springs, California, where Admiral Evans recuperated on the visit of the Atlantic Fleet to the Pacific. On the Road of a Thousand Wonders. Southern Pacific." Published by Edward H. Mitchell, San Francisco, California

2. "The Navy Target before being fired at." Published by N. Moser, N.Y.

3. "The result of one round of practice firing at Magdalena Bay, Mexico, March, 1908. Each head represents a hole in the target." #2571, Published by H. H. Stratton

4. "A Glorious Christmas" (No publisher or number listed)

San Diego

1. The sixteen battleships steaming into port; "An American Fleet Souvenir Post Card" Published by Tuck, a Semco Series.

2. "California captured the Atlantic Fleet in 1908" Published by W. Kimball Briggs Co., S.F.

3. "The Fleet in California waters", copyright 1908, by H. R. Jackson No. 0027 Published by the Pillsbury Picture Co., San Francisco and Oakland, Cal.

4. "Landing at San Diego, Calif., April 11, 1908. First Landing on American soil since leaving Hampton Roads, December 16, 1907." #507, Published by H. H. Stratton

5. This card is probably only part of a foldout postcard. Pictured is the *USS Connecticut* on the front and part of the San Diego schedule on the back. Publisher unknown

6. "Off New Port, 18th April 1908" Original photo by Frank Camp

San Pedro

1. "U. S. Battleships entering San Pedro Harbor, California." No. D.115, Published by Newman Post Card Co., Los Angeles, Cal.

2. Original photo taken of Minnie Camp by her brother Frank Camp on their visit to San Pedro to see the Fleet and Maurice.

3. "The title of this view is, "Looking for Aunt Em at New Port Beach, April 18, 1908. Is she in it?" Original photo by Frank Camp

4. Boxing Carnival, Chutes Park, Los Angeles, Calif. During Fleet Week, April 18 to 25, 1908. James J. Jeffries, referee" #2508, Published by H. H. Stratton

5. The auto tour of the city showing Maurice in his auto ready for the tour. Original photo taken by Frank Camp

6. "American Battle Ships Fleet sailors barbecue held at Chutes Park, Los Angles, Cal." Original photo

7. "Sailors Barbecue at Los Angeles, California during Fleet Week, April 18-25th. Los Angels for Me." #2510, Published by H. H. Stratton

8. "My son, these are Bob Evans fighting ships from Hampton Roads. They can whip anything on earth.", Publisher unknown

9. "Welcome to the Fleet, Published by W. Kimball Briggs, Co., S. F.

Santa Barbara

1. "Battleships at Santa Barbara, Cal." Published by M. Rieder, Los Angeles, Ca., No. 5287

2. "The Potter Hotel from the Boulevard, Santa Barbara, Cal." Published by M. Rieder, Lost Angeles, Cal., No. 4507

3. "Sailors parade at the Flower Festival, Santa Barbara, Calif., April,23, 1908. #2504, Published by H. H. Stratton

4. "A Hearty Western Welcome to the Fleet" Published by W. Kimball Briggs, Co., S. F.

San Francisco

1. A Fold out card reads on the inside, "California opens wide her Golden Gate in Welcome to the Fleet", Published by Pacific Novelty Co., San Francisco

2. "Californian's Welcome the Fleet" Published by B. I. T. Co., California (L)

3. "Just Tell them that you saw me. Sayonara-Taisha" "Welcome boys in Blue, May 08", Copyright 1908 by C. A. McDonald, from the collection of (S).

4. "California opens wide her Golden Gate in Welcome to the Fleet." This is the inside of the number the one postcard.

5. "Atlantic Fleet Entering the Golden Gate, San Francisco", Original Photo

6. "Battleship fleet, S. F. May 1908", Original photo By Mr. Will Thornburg.

7. "Battle ships at night in San Francisco Bay, Cal." Published for the Geo. Salch Co., San Francisco, by M. Rieder, Los Angeles, No. 5225

8. "The Great Naval Parade at San Francisco, May 8, 1908". #2509, Published by H. H. Stratton

9. "Fleet Parade, May 1908", Published by Britton & Rev. Lithographers, S. F., Publishers of Pictorial Post Cards.

10. "Marines of the Pacific Fleet, S. F. May 7, 1908." Original Photo

11. "This is a picture taken by one of the boys in the office and is of Fighting Bob and Mayor Taylor." Copyright 1908 by C. H. Jensen, an original photo.

12. "Marines coming ashore! Arrival Atlantic Fleet S.F. May 6th 1908" Original photo (L)

13. "Welcome to Our Boys – California 1908", Published by Britton & Rey (L)

14. "Welcome to the Fleet by the Golden Gate State", Copyright 1908 by C. E. Davis, Published by Pacific Novelty Co. #10 San Francisco, CA

15. Leather postcard, images are several battleships embossed in fine leather and inscribed "US Fleet Entering Golden Gate, Copyright 1908 by S. F. art Leather Co." (L)

16. "With the Great American Battle Fleet, *USS Minnesota*" San Francisco Bay 1908 on the top right and Hampton Roads on the top left. Novelty, S. F., Published by Universal Photographic Novelty Co.

17. "The Loure, San Francisco's Leading Restaurant". An advertisement serving German beers located on corner of Fillmore and Eddy Streets showing Evans as the "Man of the Hour".

18. "Your sailor boy arrived OK " Lettering is in gold sparkles over blue ink, Published by Cardinell – Vincent Co.

19. An original photo taken as a souvenir of Fleet Week.

20. "MJB Coffee" MJ Brandenstein Co. sent out this card to customers inviting them to come to SF during Fleet Week to see their new building as it had one of the grandest views to observe the fleet.

21. Lake Merritt, Oakland, Cal., Published by Pacific Novelty Co.

22. "Welcome Heroes" by Marlen E. Peu, Copyright in 1908 by C. A. McDonald

23. "Sailor Boys We Welcome You", Publisher unknown (L)

24. "Vallejo Welcomes the Fleet", Original Photo

25. "California's Welcome to the Fleet, San Francisco, May 1908." By Bretton & Rey, Lithographers, Published by Pictorial Post

Washington

1. "Atlantic Fleet in Bellingham, Wash. Harbor, May 23, 1908. Said to be the finest harbor in the world." Published by C T Co. of Chicago. An undivided card.

2. "Welcome to our Fleet, Seattle, May 24-26 Publisher unknown (L)

3. "Battleship Fleet Entering Seattle Harbor", Original Photo

4. "Visiting the Ships at Seattle Washington, May 27-1908" Published by H. H. Stratton, #2561

5. "Seattle Illuminations, in honor or the Atlantic Fleet, May 1908, First Ave., looking North." Original Photo (L)

6. "The Naval Parade at Seattle Washington, May 26, 1908." Published by H. H. Stratton, #2506

7. "Atlantic Fleet Entering Puget Sound" Copyright 1908 by Asahel Curtis, Roman's Photo Co. Seattle

8. "Sailors Parade, Tacoma, Washington, May 27th." #2520, Published by H. H. Stratton

9. "Greetings from California, *USS Vermont*". One of a series of cards depicting each ship on the cruise, published by Allen Fanjoy Pub. Ocean Park, Cal.

10. "Cruise of the Battleship Fleet, 1907-08-09" A map showing the position of the Fleet each day at noon. Publisher unknown (L)

Hawai'i

1. "Greetings from California, the *USS Glacier*" Part of a series of cards depicting the ships in the cruise. Published by Allen Fanjoy, Ocean Park, Cal.

2. "Souvenir Map showing the Route taken by the Atlantic Fleet from Hampton Roads to Honolulu, Hawaii U.S.A." Published by G. J. Boisse, Honolulu, T. H.

3. "Nothing in sight for days, but 16 ships and the horizon" #2577, Published by H. H. Stratton

4. "Sailors Parade at Honolulu, Hawaiian Islands, July, 1908", #2503, Published by H. H. Stratton

5. "The folks at home have just received a set of comic Naval Post Cards, sent to them by a sailor of Admiral Evan's Fleet." (L)

6. "Washington Place, Ex-queen Liliuokalani's Home, Honolulu, T. H., undivided card, published by Wall, Nichols & Co., Ltd., Honolulu.

7. "Ex-Queen Liliuokalani's, Honolulu, T. H." Undivided card, Published by Wall, Nichols & Co., Ltd., Honolulu.

8. "Moana Hotel, Honolulu, T. H." Undivided card, Published by Wall, Nichols & Co., Ltd., Honolulu

9. "Sailors from Admiral Sperry's Fleet Bathing at Honolulu Hawaiian Islands, July, 1908" #2562, published by Stratton

10. "The *Minnesota* bringing Fleet Mail from Honolulu" Copyright 1909 by Brown and Shaffer.

11. Cablegram Postcard showing the map of the cable. Maurice writes: "July 18 08 at 2:15 PM from Maurice Blair of the *USS Virginia*, Honolulu. Fine trip uneventful voyage Big reception to Fleet town decorated beautiful place arrived July 16 12 PM having good time wish you were here temperature noon today 80 degrees Hawaiians very hospitable people." Published by G.J. Boisse, Honolulu, T. H.

Auckland, New Zealand

1. "New Zealand Welcomes the American Fleet", Published by "Graphic", C.B. & Co. Lt D.S. Regd

2. "Dawn" Auckland Harbour, Arrival of the American Fleet, Original photo. (L)

3. "Recreation and Stag 'Hop' on board a U. S. Battleship", published by J. M. Colasanti

4. "U. S. Fleet entering Auckland Harbour Sunday August 9th, 1908", Publisher: Clark & Matheson, this is part of a series printed for the occasion.

5. "Queen Street, Auckland, NZ", Publisher: Empire (L)

6. "Auckland from St. Mathew's Tower", Souvenir Post Card, Visit of American Fleet to Auckland, New Zealand, August, 1908

7. "Reception to the American Fleet at Auckland, New Zealand, Aug. 9, 1908" #2568, Stratton

8. "Lunching on the domain after the parade at Auckland, New Zealand. #2521, Stratton

9. "New Zealand Souvenir, August, 1908. History of the United States of America in a Hundred Words" On the front: "Have you ever worn Roslyn Unshrinkable all-wool underwear (for men, women and children)?" Published, "Roslyn Post Card"

10. Māori Cooking operations Rotorua N. Z., Published by W. Beattie & Co. Auckland, N.Z.

11. "Australia Welcomes America", Published by Osboldstone and Attkins (L)

12. "Uncle Sam in Australia", "Correct Map of Australia" Published by Marchant and Co. Ltd. (L)

13. "U.S.A. Fleet Welcome to Australia" W. T. P Publisher (L)

14. "Australia Welcomes America" (L)

Sydney, Australia

1. "Welcome to Australia" Publisher not listed on card (L)

2. "Australia Welcomes Uncle Sam and his Fleet" Copyright 1908

3. "Welcome to Australia", Published by Osboldstone & Attkins (L)

4. "American Fleet entering Harbour", Original photo (L)

5. "Queens Statue, Sydney Illuminations, USA Fleet Visit" (L)

6. "State Entertainments" Sydney Events on the left of the card, Melbourne events on the right. Published by W. T. P.

7. "Fleet Week in Sydney. The Customs House." Published by the Commonwealth of Australia H.B.

8. "Entrance Martin Place, Sydney, USA Fleet Visit" Hand colored

9. Hand colored private mailing card

10. "The Great Naval Parade of American Sailors at Sydney, Australia, August 23, 1908", Published by Stratton, #2502

11. "American Procession, Martin Place Sydney", Hand colored Photo

12.   "Admiral Sperry Passing the Exchange, Sydney" Publisher unknown (L)

13.   "Sailors Excursion to Black Heath, Australia in the Blue Mountains 75 miles inland from Sydney, August 22, 1908" Published by Stratton, #2556

14.   "Maypole Dance Fleet - USA Fleet Celebrations" #312, hand colored, Published by Empire (L)

15.   "A Footprint of Memory", Published by the Commonwealth of Australia, (L)

Melbourne, Australia

1.   "Greetings to Our American Friends" Published by ECA (L)

2.   Admiral Sperry, Printed in Australia, W.T.P. Postcard

3.   "Disembarking at Port Melbourne, Australia, Aug. 31st, 1908" Published by Stratton, #2552

4.   "Souvenir of United States Fleet's Visit to Australia 1908 Flinders Street, Melbourne" M. S. Series

5.   "Australia Welcomes the Fleets" "With compliments from Tye & Co. Prop. LTD., House furnishers"

6.   "Australians Welcome American 1908" Published by the Commonwealth of Australia, New South Wales

7.   "The Naval Parade of American Sailors at Melbourne, Australia, August 31, 1908" Published by Stratton

8.   "Hands Across the Sea", U. S. M Series, The original owner has written, Leo for the US sailor and Joey for the Australian (L)

9.   "Hail Columbia", "Australia Greets her American Cousins" In God We Trust" Published by Empire Post Card

10.   "Drink Resch's Lager & Ales, Australia unites in greeting America"

11.   "They look well together don't you think? Gee! Same Stars! Same Strips! Eh, what? Yew see, they belong to the same familee, both 'chips' of the same 'old block'", Published by Osboldstone and Attkins, signed by Alec Barr (From Les Cowman's collection)

12.   "On march From Port Melbourne to the City of Melbourne Aug. 31, 1908" Published by Stratton

13.   "Hands Across the Sea" "They're 'in it' with you, to 'see it thru', Brave Boys from the 'Land of the Free'; May you ever maintain an endless chain of 'Hands Across the Sea' Signed by Alec Barr

14.   "Souvenir Welcome to Our American Comrades" "Hail Columbia! From the Forests, wattle scented, from the rolling Downs and Plain comes a joyous salutation to our kin From o'er the main. And 'tis echoed in the cities – wafted far upon the breeze, 'Tis Australia's joyous welcome to her comrades 'cross the seas.'"

15. Copyright, W.T.P. (L)
16. "America's Might" fac–smilie reproduction of large picture worked on silk on the Light Running NEW HOME Sewing Machine. . .as a souvenir of the visit of the United States of America Fleet, Sydney Australia 1908, Published by J. W. Johnston & Co.
17. "The people of the Southern Cross Offer Greetings to the kinsmen of the Stars and Stripes" (L)

Albany, Australia

1. "Welcome Arch, Albany, West Australia in honor of American Battleship Fleet, Sept 9, 1908" A private photo by L.M. Tough
2. "Strength, Unity, Peace Welcome" Admiral Sperry on the left, the Admiral of the *UMS Powerful* on the right.

Manila

1. Singalong Garden, Manila, P.I.
2. "US Battleship Wisconsin, Launched in San Francisco, Cal." Published by A.C. Bosselman & Co., N.Y.

Japan

1. "Welcome" Issued by the Department of Communications in Commemoration of the Visit of the American Fleet, Oct.1908
2. "The *Virginia* taking one over her bow." Original photo, Copyright 1909 by Brown and Shaffer
3. "The *Wisconsin* in a Typhoon. China Sea" Original Photo, Copyright 1909 by Brown and Shaffer
4. "The *Virginia* going on a heavy swell." Original Photo, Copyright 1909 by Brown and Shaffer
5. "*USS Rhode Island* in a storm." Original Photo, Copyright 1909 by Brown and Shaffer
6. "Speed trial scene *USS Georgia*, 1908, #185, Original Photo, copyright in 1909 by B & S
7. "Welcome" Nozawaya Dept Store, Yokohama, Japan" (S)
8. American Fleet steaming into port with the post mark, Commemoration of Visit of American Fleet 18-24 October 1908" (S)
9. From the collection of Dr. Steve Levine
10. "Welcome. Looking forward to Welcoming you all. Mitsukoshi Gofukuten. Tokyo, Japan, the Department Store."

11. "Welcome – "The ploughs were used about 1,000 years ago in ancient China. We are the originator and the greatest of the chemical fertilizers in Japan. The Phosphatic Fertilizer Factory" (S)

12. From the collection of Dr. Steve Levine

13. "Welcome Kamigataya, Ginza, Tokyo, Japan" (S)

14. "Decoration at Yokohama" (L)

15. "Decoration for U.S.A. Flee Tvisitto, Yokohama" (S)

16. "Theater Street, Yokohama: Part of a hand colored set issued in honor of the Fleet

17. "Custom House" Yokohama (L)

18. "The living arch erected for the visit of the Fleet" (L)

19. Admiral Sperry on the newly constructed pier. Sailors coming on shore

20. "My Kingdom for a Geisha Girl." F. L. 424, Copyright 1907 by the Rolograph Co. N. Y.

21. "Decorations for the Fleet Visit"

22. "Mintobashi-dori, Yokohama, Japan" (L)

23. From the collection of Dr. Steve Levine

24. "Souvenir of the Visit of the American Fleet to Japan October 1908" (S)

25. "Gate Made to Welcome the American Fleet Tokyo, Japan", Published by Stratton, #2569

26. The newly constructed pier, sailors coming ashore (L)

27. "Welcome Decorations for American Fleet" (S)

28. "The Tokyo Railway Company. To commemorate the coming of Japan's respected and most welcome visitors from the Great Neighboring Republic. October, 1908"

29. "Grand Hotel in Yokohama" #Y307 (L)

30. Part of a series of six, printed in Japan

31. "Admiral Sperry coming up the gang plank" (L)

32. "Admiral Sperry and Sailors watching the Geisha performance at Yokohama Garden Party, Oct 15 08" Published by Stratton, #2519

33. "Moonlight on the Sound, Yokohama, Japan", hand painted card.

34. "Mt Fuji" hand painted card

35. American and Japanese Flags crossed (L)

36. Nine pictures surround an American Battleship showing the tourist attractions in Japan. One of a series of six cards.

37. "US Cdr. Vice Admiral Sperry and Japanese Admiral Ito" (L)

38. "Admiral Sperry issued by the Department of Communications of a the Visit of the American Fleet Oct. 1908".

39. The *USS Connecticut* in the center, Admiral Sperry in the top right corner, flags crossed in the top left corner. (L)

40. President Roosevelt and Emperor Meiji. (L)

China

1. "Marines taking a Rickshaw ride in Cheffo, China." Published by H. Stratton

2. Seven pictures on one card: Top left; "Torpedo Boats before entering the harbour of Hong Kong", Top Right; "American Fleet entering the harbour of Hong Kong", Middle Right; "Public Gardens", Center; "VSS Monterey", Right Middle; "Happy Valley", Lower Left; "Queens Road Central", Lower Right; "Panorama of Hong Kong". Published by M. Sternberg, Hong Kong

3. "The Entertainment of the officers of the American Fleet in Amoy" Published by Yee Wo Shing, Dealer in Postcards, stamps and novels, 7 Canton Road, Kowloon

Back to Manila

1. "Manila's Welcome Arch in honor of the Visit of the American Fleet", Published by Stratton

2. Botanical Garden, Manila, P.I.

3. Street in Pandacan, Manila, P.I.

4. "Flying a 'homeward-bound pennant.'" Published by the Middlesex Company, Middletown, Conn.

5. "U.S. Battleship Fleet in Philippine Waters, A Philippine Souvenir", copyright by M. Aronson

6. "Flying a 'homeward-bound pennant.'" Published by the Middlesex Company, Middletown, Conn.

En Route to Colombo

1. *USS Virginia* (Battleship #13), taking one over her bow, Collection of Chief Quartermaster John Harold. U.S. Naval History and Heritage Command

Colombo, Ceylon

1. Sailors visiting Ceylon during voyage of Great White Fleet in 1908, Collection from Naval History and Heritage Command, Washington, DC

2. "Lake road, Colombo" Copyright No. 5. 53 The Colombo Apothecaries Col, Ltd.

3. "Enjoying a pleasant ride in Kandy, Ceylon." Published by TC Co., Chicago, from the original photograph Pub. By Brown & Shaffer, Newport News, VA (L)

Suez

1. "At the Sphinx, Egypt" Published by Stratton, #2572
2. R 126 Les Pyramides de Gizeh – Pyramids of Gizeh
3. "Le Caire Ascension of the Grand pyramid for a tourist" Published in Le Caire by Max H. Rudmann
4. "The Holy Carpet. United States Atlantic Fleet, Our Travels in Egypt on January 1909", Published by, Max H. Rudmann, Le Caire

Gibraltar

1. "Sailors from the Battle Fleet viewing the ruins in Messina, Sicily, destroyed by earthquake, Dec. 28, 1908", Published by Stratton, #2559
2. Messina, (L)
3. (L)
4. (L)
5. "Scene at Algiers, Africa during the visit of the American Fleet", Published by Stratton, #2576
6. "Souvenir of Turkey, November 24, 1908"
7. "Welcome" Union Postale Universelle
8. Three cards when put together form the "View of Harbour with British, American and Russian Fleets, 31, 1909"

Return to Hampton Roads:

1. "Homeward Bound – Meet me at Hampton Roads, Feb 21, 1909, *USS Kearsarge*", Published by Graf, Printer, USS Kearsarge
2. "February 22, 1909 Battleship Fleet entering Hampton Roads. Twenty five Battleships in line." Original photo published by Abbe. N. News, Va.
3. "The *Mayflower* with President Roosevelt on board awaiting the return of the Fleet to Hampton Roads, Feb. 22, 1909." Published by Stratton, #2573
4. "Awaiting the Return of the Fleet at Old Point Comfort, VA. Feb. 22, 1909", Published by Stratton, #2554
5. "Sailors Parade at Norfolk, VA. Feb. 27, 1909 after the return from the 'Trip Around the World'", Published by Stratton, #2557
6. "Resting in front of the Naval Y.M.C.A. building, Norfolk, VA after parade. Feb 27, 1908" (Misprint on the card, it should read, 1909) Published by Stratton
7. "Dec. 1907 Around the World Feb 1909 Souvenir Return of the Fleet, Norfolk, VA." The sixteen Battleships are "traveling" around the picture of two men. An Original photo

8. "At Home Again" Printed in Germany

9. "I have been to the West Indies, South American, Around the Horn, Chili, Mexico, to New Zealand, Australia, The Philippines, Japan, China, East Indies, Egypt, Italy, Spain and other places, but I don't remember ever being THERE.", Published by Middlesex Company. (S)

Last page (122)

10. "Hurrah for the U.S.", The Ullman Mfg. Co, NY, 1909. American Postcard, North Pole series, #162

HURRAH FOR U.S.